RAPA NUI

....

PETE WRIGHT

Richmond Publishing
4 King Street Cloisters
Albion Place
London W6 0QT
United Kingdom

© La Spiga languages 2004
This edition published by Richmond Publishing® 2004

ISBN:84-668-0485-4

Printed in Italy by Techno Media Reference

Text: Pete Wright

Notes and exercises: Rachel Roberts

Cover: Valentine Bilet

Editing: Mary Hampton

PREFACE

Far out in the lonely Pacific Ocean, there is an island of mystery.

The island waits, windy and wave-beaten.

The stone statues near the rocky shore stare out over the ever-changing and eternal sea.

The people who carved them, and left them there, have vanished from the earth, leaving behind only their greatness.

Secrets. Secrets of how and why.

The secrets of Rapa Nui *lie deep and hidden.*

Over the wind-blown, warm, grass-covered earth, the islanders have a calm and settled life.

Now, their peace is threatened.

Their fragile world is about to be turned upside-down.

There is a new force on the island.

There are new people here.

Isolation is no longer a protection.

The world is a small place for money, for travel, for greed.

The great statues are to become toys — toys in the hands of the rich.

But, somewhere, eyes watch, and see what is to come.

How far would you go to protect the people you love?

What is your way of life worth?

From the past, comes a terrible answer…

* N.B. Some of the more difficult words in the text have been written in phonetic symbols to help you with the pronunciation.

Moai, Ahu Vaiuri at Tahai

1 • Mayor Pro Tem

Mayor Pro Tem appeared to be an odious[1] man. He knew it. He cultivated[2] it. He loved it!

Odious people are above suspicion; they are people with only two dimensions – flat and obvious.

"Carter, you know my policy: we want tourism up, up, up, on this island – let's make some money!"

Carter, the 'Big Businessman' from Florida State, U.S.A., shifted in the deep, leather armchair in the Mayor's office.

"Ye-es," he answered, laconically[3].

"Carter," Mayor Pro Tem puffed at his cigar enthusiastically, "Carter, what do I always say? We've got to reach the 'critical mass'. What do I say?"

"Yeah, yeah, yeah. I've heard all this. You want to reach a 'critical mass' of American tourists, and then we're – how do you put it?"

"… and then we're talking!"

"Right."

The Mayor watched the smoke from his cigar drift towards the ceiling. He fingered the long lobe of one ear. The light skin of his face was topped by thick reddish-brown hair. His eyes were deep set. His nose was straight, with wide, flat nostrils. His broad mouth was thin-lipped and slightly pursed[4], curving down grimly[5] at the edges – when he wasn't smiling. His jaw was strong.

1. **odious:** hateful, offensive.
2. **cultivated:** looked after (here, encouraged).
3. **laconically:** /læˈkɒnɪklɪ/ speaking with few words.
4. **pursed:** /pɜːst/ contracted in tight wrinkles.
5. **grimly:** without humour, very seriously.

Carter watched the man sitting opposite him. The face seemed somehow familiar.

"I've got it!" exclaimed[6] Carter, excitedly.

"What is it that you've got?"

"I've just realised who you remind me of."

"And who is that?"

"Harvey Keitel, the American actor. He's done lots of movies – *Reservoir Dogs, Pulp Fiction…*"

"Ah!" said the Mayor, "I know the man. And didn't he do *The Piano*?"

"Search me," said Carter, "a lot of movie stars can play an instrument."

II • Carter

Carter thought Mayor Pro Tem was an odious man, but odious men could be useful. He'd had enough of Environmentalists, Government Agencies, Investors with no guts[1]. He knew people like Mayor Pro Tem. They were peasants[2]. They had the cunning[3] of the peasant – like the cunning of a fox: shallow, narrow-minded, and totally selfish. You knew where you were with people like the Mayor. They did all the foot-work in big business ventures[4], and, when they had cleared a path, powerful people like Carter himself drove in with their smooth,

6. **exclaimed:** said with surprise or annoyance.

1. **guts:** slang for courage.

2. **peasants:** /'pezənts/ (uneducated) workers on the land.

3. **cunning:** crafty, clever at winning.

4. **ventures:** attempts or processes.

Cadillac money, and the rolling wheels of Wall Street. And behind them came solid, blue-suited attorneys[5], taking anything worth having.

Mayor Pro Tem would be more than grateful for the crumbs that fell from the table of the real money-men. Everyone would be happy. It was the way of the world.

III • The Island

Where are we? We are in Hanga Roa, tiny 'capital' of a thirty-kilometre volcanic dot in the wide Pacific Ocean, thousands of kilometres from anywhere.

EASTER ISLAND – RAPA NUI – The island of mystery; island of wonders; island of magnificent stone statues, ten or twenty metres high, dotting the landscape; island of beautifully crafted stone platforms[1] set in bleak[2] but wonderful hills.

The coast of razor sharp volcanic rocks is battered by the long, Pacific waves. It is a land of wind and grass; of scattered, dead volcanos; of gentle hills, looking as if they were fashioned[3] by human hands out of the open, black-pebbled[4] grassland; of wild horses, sheep and silence; of moody, changeable weather. A land of contrast with the high, wide expanse of a

---

5. **attorneys:** /əˈtɜːnɪz/ lawyers.
1. **platforms:** a large, raised, constructed surface.
2. **bleak:** dull and without comfort.
3. **fashioned:** made.
4. **pebbled:** with many small, smooth stones.

sky. A land without song-birds. Only the silent, hunting hawks[5] skim[6] the earth. This dry, dry land, Rapa Nui, with water found only in the deep crater[7] lakes of Rana Kao, Roi and Roraka.

The inhabitants have no more history than the tales of a few generations. They are self-contained, friendly, mutually supportive. They supervise their herds of horses and flocks of sheep in this unfenced land. Their few cows give milk, the sea gives fish. The people are patient, and accept the exodus of many of their number to Chile, as they accept the influx[8] of new settlers[9].

Above all, Rapa Nui – Easter Island – has an aching sense of something about to happen, of expectancy. The winds have twenty names. The weather changes suddenly. It is a landscape of moods[10], of intensity.

I will tell you all that is known by the white men about Easter Island.

Long, long ago – perhaps two millennia – there lived a race of people who, after many centuries of work, left the most wonderful monuments, who filled the landscape of their homeland with statues, pictures and structures, but whose writings were few and indecipherable[11].

5. **hawks:** hunting bird.
6. **skim:** here, fly low over.
7. **crater:** the open inner surface of a volcano.
8. **influx:** the coming in of.
9. **settlers:** people arriving to live, not to visit.
10. **moods:** here, strong atmospheres.
11. **indecipherable:** /ɪndɪˈsaɪfrəbəl/ unable to be translated or understood.

When they arrived, they burned the native forests, until all but a few trees surviving on the peaks[12] were gone. They planted sweet potatoes. They grew reeds[13] in the lakes in the volcano craters, creating swamps[14] under the hot, tropical sun.

Their skin was white. Their hair was reddish brown. They lived side by side with the dark-skinned Polynesians who also found a home on the island. They thrived[15].

IV • The First Statue

A statue was carved from the volcanic rock using tiny, hard, stone tools. The face of the statue was arrogant[1] and superior. The tall, narrow forehead was topped with a hat of red stone. The eye sockets were sightless. The nose was proud. The thin-lipped mouth was wide and severe[2]. It was the prototype[3] God of the island.

When the most important leaders of the people died, their bodies were laid under the stone platforms. Memory of them was preserved in larger and larger copies of the prototype. These were set, shoulder to shoulder, on the platforms aligned with the sun.

12. **peaks:** the highest places.
13. **reeds:** plants that grow in wet condition, with stems that can be used for roofs, etc.
14. **swamps:** watery ground with vegetation.
15. **thrived:** /θraɪvd/ lived very successfully.
 1. **arrogant:** feeling too much importance.
 2. **severe:** very strict.
 3. **prototype:** /ˈprəʊtətaɪp/ the first version of something.

After anonymous ages, a millennium and a half, there came a time when everything stopped. The stone-carvers' tools were left where they lay. This culture with no weapons suddenly had volcanic glass arrow[4] heads. No one knows what happened. The stone carving stopped. The statues awaiting delivery to the platforms around the island were left where they stood, gazing[5] forever over the wide ocean from the grassy slope between the quarry[6] and the shore.

When the first white men appeared, centuries later, greedy[7] for power, information, and then slaves, there was only a savage remnant[8] of the light- and dark-skinned people. The slave merchants stripped the island.

Today, the few inhabitants live their friendly, calm lives, with their roaming herds of sheep and horses, and their occasional cattle. They watch the steady influx of visitors; see the foreign eyes drink in this fresh wonder of the world.

The island waits. Always, something is waiting just out of sight. Something is about to happen.

4. **arrow:** a projectile fired from a bow.
5. **gazing:** looking in a fixed way.
6. **quarry:** here, a place where rock is dug from.
7. **greedy:** with an over-strong appetite for.
8. **savage remnant:** uncivilized remainder.

V • Rana Kao

Carter thought his heart was going to burst. The steep climb up the side of the volcano, Rana Kao, near the town, had almost killed him. Mayor Pro Tem was a big man, but he seemed fresh and enthusiastic.

"I must sit down for a moment," gasped Carter.

"Carter, look at this wonderful view over the island. I am reminded of the Devil's temptation[1] of Christ. The Devil took Jesus up into a high place and offered[2] him all that he could see.

"Carter, pay attention, all of this can be yours!" The Mayor exploded into a huge laugh. The red faced Carter was preoccupied at this moment with his mortality[3], and not with 'real estate'[4].

The view was magnificent. The only sound was the wind rushing over the short, pale yellow grass.

"Keep your hat on, Carter. You'll burn in this sun."

Then, far below, three horses chased[5] playfully across the hillside, their manes[6] flying. Their shrill cries carried on the wind. Out of sight, sheep called to each other.

"I love this land, Carter. Carter, are you OK? Yes? We'll walk slowly round to the other side of the volcano, overlooking the sea. I'll show you something."

He took the American's arm and helped him along the narrow track[7]. Soon, Carter recovered enough

1. **temptation:** a persuasion to do something that is wrong.
2. **offered:** proposed to give something.
3. **mortality:** possibility of dying.
4. **'real estate':** buildings or land as property.
5. **chased:** pursued.
6. **manes:** long hair on a horse's neck.
7. **track:** a small path made by being walked on.

from the hard climb to take an interest in his surroundings.

"Here we are, my friend. Let's stop for some refreshment. We're a bit sheltered[8] here. As soon as we go round that corner, we'll feel the full force of the wind. You're not as unfit as I thought you were." Mayor Pro Tem could now sense the hard muscle under the layer of fat on Carter's body. He treated the American with a new respect[9].

VI • Bird-man

"Spectacular!" From the rim[1] of the volcano, the ground dropped away in sheer cliffs. Five hundred metres or more below, the sea pounded the black, rocky shore. The surf cannoned[2] into the cracks and flew up high in the air. Behind them, three hundred metres below their feet, was the floor of the crater, fifteen hundred metres across.

"Carter, look down there." The Mayor pointed out to sea.

Carter felt a little giddy[3]. He sat down on his heels to steady himself. His hands gripped the dark rock. He felt safer.

"Where?" he asked.

"Do you see those three little islands below? There, in the sea."

8. **sheltered:** protected from the weather.
9. **respect:** consideration, to value someone.
1. **rim:** narrow, circular, top edge.
2. **cannoned:** hit forcefully.
3. **giddy:** /ˈgɪdɪ/ unable to maintain balance.

"Yeah. What about them?"

The Mayor looked thoughtfully along the rim of the volcano.

"There was a ceremonial[4] village near here. The inhabitants lived in caves[5]. They had a special ceremony each Spring."

"Yeah?"

"Yes. We call it the ceremony of the 'Bird-man'."

"What was that?"

"Well, Carter, the young men would test their strength and courage by swimming out to those islands on little reed floats[6]. The first one to bring back a bird's egg would be the 'Bird-man'."

"Bird-man! They must have been mad! No-one could survive[7] in a sea like that."

"I'm sure a lot of them didn't! The title of Bird-man must have been a very high honour[8]." Mayor Pro Tem looked down at the smooth skin on his arms criss-crossed[9] by the fine, white lines of old scars[10]. He was suddenly lost in old memories.

4. **ceremonial:** of ceremony, or ritual.
5. **caves:** spaces in rock with access from the outside.
6. **floats:** something to help buoyancy or ability to stay up in water.
7. **survive:** manage to live.
8. **honour:** worthy of much respect.
9. **criss-crossed:** of lines, many going at right angles to each other.
10. **scars:** the trace on the skin left by healed cuts or burns.

VII • The Statues, The Platforms

Carter, the businessman from Florida, turned away from the terrifying drop into the sea.

"Mayor, why did you bring me up here? What was it you wanted to 'show' me?"

Mayor Pro Tem smiled at Carter's shrewdness[1]. He sucked at his teeth, thoughtfully.

"Mr Carter, there are two things that you can see up here that you could not understand if I tried to explain them to you in my office back in town."

Carter looked at the Mayor with hard, appraising[2] eyes.

"First – I want you to appreciate[3] that the 'gravity'[4] of Rapa Nui is different from any other place in the world." Mayor Pro Tem leaned down and picked up a piece of stone. He closed his fingers. It disappeared from view. He opened his fingers. The stone sat in the palm of his hand.

"The platforms on which the statues used to stand are made out of blocks of stone, some of them many tonnes in weight." The Mayor took a small penknife out of his pocket and opened the blade. Carter stiffened slightly. The Mayor grinned, and continued.

"If you took this blade and ran it round the edge of one of those stone blocks where it joins the surrounding blocks, each block is so finely made, that you could not find a gap[5] wide enough to push this blade into. Not

---

1. **shrewdness:** /ʃryːdnəs/ cleverness, ability to understand complex situations.
2. **appraising:** looking carefully to understand.
3. **appreciate:** here, feel and understand.
4. **'gravity':** here, the sense of weight.
5. **gap:** a space where two things join.

13

only are the platforms beautifully crafted, they have shape and decoration far beyond the simply functional. They are works of art."

"And?" said Carter, wanting Mayor Pro Tem to make his point in everyday business language, so that it would seem more 'affordable', 'containable', or something… something less 'alien'[6].

The other man tossed[7] the small stone to the American.

"My dear Carter, the platforms, the statues, everything, were made with tools identical to the one you hold in your hand – that's not an ordinary stone – it's an actual stone-age tool. I want you to understand that what happened on this island has involved a human endeavour[8], discipline[9] and commitment[10] that you can only dream of."

Carter turned away, and looked at the precipice[11] of black rock.

"Well, Mr Mayor, while we walk back, perhaps you will tell me what else you want me to understand." It seemed crazy, but he knew he would feel safer with this man away from the huge drop to the remorseless[12] sea churning[13] far below.

After a while, they were back round the crater again, with a fine view of most of the island stretching out into the distance.

6. 'alien': totally foreign.
7. tossed: threw casually.
8. endeavour: /en'devə/ an attempt to achieve something.
9. discipline: organisation and regulation.
10. commitment: determination to do something.
11. precipice: /'presɪpɪs/ a high, vertical cliff.
12. remorseless: /rɪ'mɔːsləs/ unceasing, merciless.
13. churning: /'tʃɜːnɪŋ/ forceful, heavy stirring.

"Well?" said Carter, raising his eyebrows.

Mayor Pro Tem smiled.

"The other thing I want you to understand, is that I, Mayor Pro Tem, born on this island of Rapa Nui, know just how much of this glorious, singular, and irreplaceable item[14] of God's universe we are about to destroy under the boots of a million visitors."

With that, he set off striding[15] down the slope, lighting his cigar as he walked, and blowing smoke into the innocent morning air.

VIII • The Developers

The small jet from Chile, the nearest land mass, bumped down on the short runway at Hanga Roa with small puffs of burning rubber. It decelerated quickly, and taxied to the reception building. Twelve passengers stepped onto the tarmac[1]. Two men welcomed them, and led them to waiting cars which sped to the office of Mayor Pro Tem.

The Mayor lowered the blinds[2] on the windows of the large room. The bright day was excluded. The huge table was loaded with bundles of drawings, stacks of papers, and an assortment[3] of very expensive lap-top computers.

Carter introduced Mayor Pro Tem.

14. **item**: /ˈaɪtəm/ a single thing.
15. **striding**: walking with long steps.
 1. **tarmac**: a type of road surface.
 2. **blinds**: window coverings.
 3. **assortment**: a collection of different types.

"This, ladies and gentleman, is my friend, Mayor Pro Tem. He is perhaps the most unscrupulous[4] man on the island – after me, of course."

There was a buzz[5] of polite amusement from the listeners.

"Yesterday, the Mayor chose a very novel[6] way to demonstrate to me his total commitment to our transformation of this island – Easter Island – into one of the newest and most exciting tourist venues for the rich – the very rich – American traveller."

A lady among the listeners raised her hand slightly, and asked, "Does Mr Pro Tem have extensive land rights on the island? Does he have large resources? In short, what is he offering?"

Carter looked a little embarrassed by the directness of the lady's question.

The Mayor seemed unconcerned.

"Madam, you are from England, are you not? I recognise your accent. What did your poet say? – 'Between the idea and the reality, falls the shadow'. I'm sure you recognise the lines. Mr Carter has the idea, you and your colleagues have the means[7] to make it a reality, and I – as I am sure you already know from your extensive research – am able to deal with our particular shadow. So…?"

The lady settled back in her chair. The business of turning the island into a major American tourist destination began in earnest[8].

---

4. **unscrupulous:** /ʌnˈskruːpjələs/ without conscience.
5. **buzz:** a noise like a bee makes.
6. **novel:** here, new and surprising.
7. **means:** here, tools or facilities.
8. **in earnest:** in a serious, determined way.

IX • Construction Begins

In the weeks and months that followed, the islanders seemed to accept the massive expansion of the island's infrastructure[1] – the hotels, the airport, the hospital, the power supplies and services, the transport and communications systems, even the private security force[2] brought in to police the island.

At first, Carter assumed that the indigenous[3] population were so reserved, friendly and respectful, that they did not understand the threat[4] to their island's tranquillity.

Then he imagined that Mayor Pro Tem must be placating[5] the locals with fabulous promises of wealth and prosperity for the people who co-operated with the tourist business.

In the end, he came to believe that it was the Easter Islanders' complete trust[6] in Mayor Pro Tem himself, that allowed them to sit by while the all-powerful American Dream was plugged into[7] this island, to be washed in the long waves of the Pacific.

Even Carter was impressed by the speed of construction. Everything was modular. Buildings, bridges, power plants, all that was needed was flown in, or arrived by boat, to be unloaded, placed, and bolted together. The hotel rooms came complete

1. **infrastructure:** basic facilities a society needs in order to function.
2. **security force:** people employed to act as a police force.
3. **indigenous:** the original.
4. **threat:** the direct nearness of something bad happening.
5. **placating:** soothing, or making feel satisfied.
6. **trust:** confidence in.
7. **plugged into:** inserted in.

with curtains, carpet and bed linen. Air conditioners blew chill air into new, hermetically sealed spaces.

The islanders tended[8] their livestock, went to church on Sundays, and generally got on with their lives. The construction workers watched the islanders with suspicion and quiet contempt[9].

Mayor Pro Tem had promised that the development would not affect his people directly. He was true to his promise. So far, not a dollar found its way into the pockets of the local people. They did not seem to mind[10].

X • Two Weeks

"Well, Mayor Pro Tem, Lord of the Island," said Carter, cheerfully, "in two weeks, the first batch[1] of two thousand visitors – among whom will be many celebrities – will arrive."

"I have looked forward to that day, Mr Carter, ever since I first realised the tourism potential[2] of this little island of ours."

"And we've only just begun," said Carter, rubbing his hands together, "and I'm very pleased that you did not include all your friends and relatives in the operation. My colleagues would not have been very understanding if you had!"

"Carter, Carter. What can I say? Too many cooks

8. **tended:** looked after.
9. **contempt:** lack of respect.
10. **to mind:** to care.

1. **batch:** a number of things ready at one time.
2. **potential:** the possibility that something can happen.

spoil the soup, eh? In fact, I don't have many relatives among the locals you have met so far. My people keep themselves to themselves. The other islanders are happy to leave things to me."

"Good man," said Carter, warmly. What he was actually thinking was, "Poor fool!"

XI • A Lesson in Manners [1]

"Mayor Pro Tem, it's time for you to earn your pay!" The Mayor looked up from his desk. One of Carter's assistants had entered his office. He hadn't knocked. He hadn't introduced himself. His short, rude [2] statement was more suited [3] to the bullying of an employee.

"Mr... er?"

"My name is Irving, George Irving. I..."

"Mr Irving – Mr George Irving – tell me something: could this project be accomplished without Mr Carter?"

The young man seemed surprised at such an obvious question.

"No, of course not! But..."

"And, could this project be accomplished without me?"

"Well, no, I suppose not."

"Lastly, could this project be accomplished without you?"

The young man was silent. Mayor Pro Tem

1. **Manners:** ways of behaviour.
2. **rude:** impolite.
3. **suited:** same as suitable, matched.

watched a contorted[4] series of emotions play about the freshly shaved face, before saying,

"I suggest that you, Mr George Irving – and anyone else you might like to suggest it to – would be wise[5] to treat me with exactly the same consideration and respect that Mr Carter enjoys. Don't you agree?"

"… Yes, sir."

XII • The 'Greens'

It was the 'Greens'. The Greens were the world's newest, and often most reactionary[1], pressure group[2]. They tried to police the environment of the world. Once, that policing was attempted by radicals[3]. Now the radicals had been superseded[4] by the chattering middle classes, who were better organised, better financed, and better placed to hold power – and there was the added attraction of the certainty of being absolutely 'right'.

The Greens were on Easter Island. Mayor Pro Tem went to meet them.

"Welcome. Ladies and gentlemen, welcome to Rapa Nui."

4. **contorted**: distorted.
5. **wise**: having wisdom or knowledge and good judgement.

1. **reactionary**: opposed to progress.
2. **pressure group**: group that works by trying to make the people who make decisions change their decisions.
3. **radicals**: here, a person with strong, unusual social ideas.
4. **superseded**: /suːpəˈsiːdɪd/ replaced by.

"Whose side are you on? Ours or theirs?"

"I hope I am on the side of the island, what else?"

Mayor Pro Tem was surrounded by a group of well-educated, well informed, well connected[5], and very dangerous people. His desire to fill the island with American tourists was seriously threatened by this small group of people.

Dealing with[6] the American businessmen was straightforward. With them, all he needed was a greedy face and a willingness to do whatever was necessary. With this 'international committee of environmentalists', it was different. He let the group explain its concerns, and waited for them to start running out of steam.

XIII • The Discussion

"Ladies and gentlemen," said Mayor Pro Tem, jumping into the first gap, "I think my desire to conserve and protect this island from the effects of insensitive and uncontrolled tourism are at least as strong as yours…"

The group of people found the suggestion that anyone could be more concerned than the experts – the specialists (themselves) – a bit difficult to accept, especially as it came from a native islander.

"I don't think you understand how powerful and unscrupulous these developers are," said a tall, thin man, with a forceful stare.

5. **well connected:** knowing and being helped by influential people.
6. **Dealing with:** managing the relationship with.

The Mayor smiled, and replied, calmly, "I know these men. I have stood beside them. I know exactly what they are like. Some of them were trained in the same schools as some of you, I believe."

The conversation started to become a backwards and forwards exchange that threatened to go on for ever. Mayor Pro Tem had an appointment with several of the local families to meet at one of their houses for a long evening of eating, drinking and celebration – a Sau Sau. He did not intend to miss it.

He interrupted a monologue from one of the Greens, to whom he had barely listened.

"Listen! Please, listen. This is the situation. I was a boy when Thor Heyerdahl came here in the fifties to investigate the ancient culture of the island. I was with him when he rescued the last seeds of the last toromiro tree from the Rano Kao crater. I was a young man when I helped replant seeds from trees grown in Sweden from those last toromiro seeds..."

The Mayor's rather[1] poetic approach to the discussion seemed to please the visitors. He continued.

"As I see it, there are two obvious possibilities for the future of Rapa Nui.

"First, since the island 'belongs' to Chile, the tourist developers can pay a large amount of money to the government of Chile for permission to do whatever they like. We would have to go all the way to Chile, with our caps[2] in our hands, to beg money for conservation work. The Chilean government would say to us that conservation is the responsibility of the islanders and the developers..."

1. **rather:** to some amount or degree.
2. **caps:** hats - 'cap in hand' means humbly, begging, asking for a favour.

The Mayor could see from the response of the conservationists that they did not like the first option[3].

"And, second, ladies and gentlemen, we could agree to receive a certain percentage of the income from tourism to finance conservation, while the developers would also pay a 'license' to Chile for the use of their island. I know which option I prefer!"

The tall, thin man with the stare offered another option.

"Or we could stop the place from becoming a holiday camp right now!"

Mayor Pro Tem could see the light of battle in the eyes of the people who surrounded him. He pictured them going away to fight the good fight on the stage of international environmental campaigns. He did not think they would succeed. He thought, perhaps, that they might slow the first influx of eager American tourists.

"That is, of course, a possibility," said the Mayor, pretending to misunderstand what had just been said.

"I imagine that something like the use of the island to test a nuclear device, or to experiment with biological warfare might be enough to keep the Americans away. However, we all know that when the American businessman scents[4] large profits in some new place in the world, he will have all the force of the political and economic machinery of the United States behind him!"

The discussion broke up into small arguments

between the Conservationists. The Mayor drifted to the edge of the group, and then walked quietly away – pleased.

XIV • Sau Sau

"What in God's name do you think you're doing, you old rascal[1]? You seem to be living in the pockets of these Americans!" The priest's voice boomed[2] out above the noise of the children running around playing among the dogs which hurtled[3] this way and that. His great bush of a beard waggled below a pair of astonishingly blue eyes.

Mayor Pro Tem looked into his glass of Pisco Sour[4].

"Trust[5] me, Father."

A background noise of laughter and conversation filled the evening air.

The priest looked over at the whole sheep roasting[6] above the fire. It was one of the thousands that 'wandered'[7] away from the government flock every year, and found themselves in the stomachs of the islanders.

1. **rascal:** someone who behaves immorally, but is more mischievous than evil.
2. **boomed:** with a loud, rounded quality.
3. **hurtled:** /ˈhɜːtəld/ moved fast and without much control.
4. **Pisco Sour:** a strong, alcoholic drink made only on the island.
5. **Trust:** here, have confidence in.
6. **roasting:** cooking by direct heat in its own fat.
7. **'wandered':** moved aimlessly, here, 'wandered' means possibly stolen.

"I trust in God – as you know. I probably trust in quite a few other things as well. But, I have a feeling that the name Mayor Pro Tem does not occur on the list[8] of things that I trust!"

The Mayor laughed heartily, and slapped his thigh. He lifted his glass to toast the island's one and only priest, and drained it in one go.

The priest smiled. He did not approve of Mayor Pro Tem. There were even some hidden depths about this man that disturbed the Catholic Father. But he liked him all the same. It was a shame[9] that the Mayor had allowed himself to be sucked into the plans of these American businessmen. No good would come of it, he was sure.

Both the Mayor and he had realised that the island was threatened by enormous changes. The old ways of life were good, but they could not be preserved[10] artificially. Each man dealt[11] with the problem in a different way. The priest tried to provide comfort and support for the difficult times ahead. He did not feel that it was his job to interfere with politics or commerce[12].

The Mayor was different. The people of the island were used to him. They accepted his rather unpleasant business activities, since he acted as a 'buffer'[13] between the islanders and the outside world. He behaved in all ways like an islander, a little reserved[14]

---

8. **list**: a number of things written down.
9. **a shame**: an unfortunate and regrettable thing.
10. **preserved**: kept going in the present form.
11. **dealt**: past of *to deal*; here, to manage.
12. **commerce**: the business of large scale buying and selling.
13. **'buffer'**: a cushion used to deaden a blow or effect.
14. **reserved**: here, withdrawn or not out-going.

perhaps, but they sensed strange desires or appetites in this big man. He was part of the island, and not part of it at the same time. The Mayor's function[15] as a representative of the islanders' interests with the outside world had expanded into something more like a partnership[16] with the outside. It was difficult for the locals to know just which side Mayor Pro Tem was on. The priest was acting as a spokesman for the community when he made the light-hearted accusation.

In the far distance, dark clouds gathered near the slopes of Rana Kao.

XV • Death

The squall[1] was very localised. Elsewhere on the island, the weather was fine. The wind whipped around the cranes and scaffolding. A stack[2] of wooden boards[3] blew over with a crash. An empty oil drum[4] tipped and rolled across an expanse of freshly poured concrete. A group of people, lit by the high floodlights, bent almost double as they ran for shelter. The stinging rain flew horizontally, tearing at their clothes and soaking them to the skin. One of the cables[5]

15. **function:** duties of a job, activity.
16. **partnership:** joining with to do something.
 1. **squall:** /skwɔːl/ a sudden, violent wind.
 2. **stack:** things placed on top of one another.
 3. **boards:** large, flat sheets of wooden material.
 4. **drum:** cylindrical steel container.
 5. **cables:** here, strong, steel wires. Electrical cables are wires for carrying electricity.

supporting a central lighting column strained and squeaked as the fierce wind attempted to throw the steel lattice to the ground. Perhaps it was a loose bolt on the clamp that held the cable to a large concrete block. Whatever the reason, the end of the cable pulled loose in a shower of sparks, as steel ground[6] on steel. The cable went slack[7] and flew away.

Like a great tree falling, the column, free from the restraining cable, tilted towards the earth with a long, protesting screech[8]. The group of running figures realised its peril[9]. They scattered. The great column of lights fell towards them. The base of the falling column hit a fuel trailer[10], and lifted wildly. The electricity cables to the lights started to snap[11]. The lights flickered off, dying red. Three people under the falling column were saved by the slope created by the fuel trailer. Two others caught the full force of the nest of flood-lights at the column's top.

Their blood steamed and boiled in the darkness against the hot lamps.

The squall ended as quickly as it had begun. The sickly smell of burnt flesh[12] spread across the scene of desolation.

6. **ground:** here, past tense of to grind.
7. **slack:** without tension.
8. **screech:** /skriːtʃ/ a loud, rough, high, unpleasant sound.
9. **peril:** personal danger.
10. **trailer:** a wheeled vehicle without an engine.
11. **snap:** break suddenly.
12. **flesh:** the muscle on a body.

XVI • The Problem

A horse galloped up to the blazing fire. The fat from the cooking meat dropped and spat flame. The horseman was obviously from the construction site. The poor beast[1] was loaded down with a heavy, cowboy-style saddle. The rider wore the yellow 'hard-hat' of a construction worker. He dismounted quickly, managing to catch his boot in the stirrup, hopped free, and then dodged[2] through the informal gathering to speak to Mayor Pro Tem.

"Can I speak to you, sir?"

"Father, please excuse me," the Mayor smiled at the priest, and then stood up to go with the visitor to the edge of the firelight. For all the Pisco Sours he had drunk that evening, he was quite steady on his feet.

"Sir, we have a problem. We need your help" said the construction worker, when he was sure they could not be overheard.

"What can I do? What's the problem?"

"There's been an accident back at the building site – a serious accident. It could mean trouble for the whole project." The man was obviously very worried.

"Let's go and see what can be done." The Mayor seemed calm[3], untroubled.

"Thank you, sir. Have you a horse?"

"No. I will go on yours."

"How will I get back…?"

"What I mean is, we will both go on your horse."

"Won't that slow us down?"

1. **beast:** here, same as animal.
2. **dodged:** /dɒdʒd/ moved erratically to avoid collision.
3. **calm:** peaceful.

"You will have plenty of time to tell me about the problem on the way."

XVII • Shadows

Mayor Pro Tem had never seen Carter look so unsettled. The developer looked up and shouted at the Mayor.

"Why are you so calm? Can't you see that this is a disaster? Are you drunk? Are you mad?!"

Mayor Pro Tem smiled in a friendly way.

"I have heard nothing to stop me being calm. No, no and no. These are the answers to your questions."

Carter threw up his arms in disbelief.

"These weren't a couple of construction workers that were killed. That would be bad enough. They were two of the world's most influential[1] environmentalists! They came over here to negotiate[2] with us. What do we do? We don't try to win them over by argument, or persuade[3] them that their concerns for this tiny bit of environment are the same as ours. No, we don't do that. We KILL THEM!"

Carter was red in the face. Mayor Pro Tem took him by the arm and seated him back in his expensive executive chair. The man looked up at him like a baby waiting to be soothed[4] by its mother.

"Mr Carter – may I call you Selwyn – it was an

---

1. **influential:** able to affect others.
2. **negotiate:** to arrange an agreement.
3. **persuade:** to influence by talk.
4. **soothed:** /suːðd/ made calm.

accident; an accident. You cannot be held responsible for acts of God."

"Where have you been all your life! This is the twenty first century! This is the age of litigation[5]. If something bad happens to someone, it doesn't matter whose fault[6] it is. Someone has to pay. We'll be paying cash, and we'll be paying with one of the worst media fiascos[7] ever. A certain group of financial backers arrive here on Monday morning to decide whether they want to pay for eighty five per cent of this whole project, or whether they want to climb back on their plane and leave this bunch of arseholes, who can't keep their building equipment off the opposition, to their sad and bankrupt[8] fate[9]!"

"Selwyn, please…"

"I don't suppose that this would be the sort of 'shadow' that – what was it? – that 'falls between the idea and the reality' and which you were hired[10] to deal with?"

"I did not anticipate[11] quite this type of problem, but the answer to your question is 'yes'."

Carter did a sort of 'double take'[12], looking more carefully at the face of the man standing beside him. After a time, his breathing became a bit easier.

"And you are 'Mr Fix-it'?" he asked.

"I am," replied the Mayor.

5. **litigation:** legal action in the courts.
6. **fault:** here, error.
7. **fiascos:** complete failures.
8. **bankrupt:** having no money and also having large debts.
9. **fate:** doom, inevitable fortune, usually bad.
10. **hired:** employed.
11. **anticipate:** foresee and prepare for something to happen.
12. **'double take':** to look twice at in surprise or curiosity.

XVIII • The Backers

A new day. Mayor Pro Tem looked across at the 'big backers' and tried to imagine what sort of animal might have the same characteristics[1]. He could think of none.

"We heard you had a little accident on Saturday night," said one of their number.

A construction worker hurried up to Carter and whispered something urgently[2] into his ear.

The Mayor smiled. "Fortunately, no one was hurt. A sudden squall brought down one of the lighting columns. No great harm was done, but it was an excellent opportunity for the emergency teams to try out their skills and organisation."

"We heard that there were injuries."

"Apparently, two sheep had wandered[3] onto the site and were the unfortunate victims[4] of the falling equipment. There are many sheep on this island – and no fences."

The backer seemed satisfied[5] with the Mayor's smooth answer.

Carter looked Mayor Pro Tem in the eye, and said, "I've just had a message that the two... er... 'victims' have disappeared from the refrigerated storage area."

The Mayor grinned. "Well, you know what we islanders are like. One must not look at the pedigree[6] of a free meal!"

---

1. **characteristics:** physical qualities.
2. **urgently:** calling for immediate action.
3. **wandered:** moved aimlessly.
4. **victims:** those hurt by some event.
5. **satisfied:** content.
6. **pedigree:** the formal record of an animal's parentage.

The group of men laughed.

Carter edged up to the Mayor after a few minutes, and murmured[7], "I have a suspicion that the rest of the 'flock' will miss their company."

"My dear Selwyn, I think the group of environmentalists are as embarrassed by the whole matter as we are. The two who died were not particularly liked."

Their quiet conversation was interrupted by a cry from one of the backers.

"Look! Look up on that volcano in the distance. There's smoke coming off the top. We thought all the volcanic activity here was long gone."

"Isn't that near where your people live, Mayor?" said Carter, sounding rather more aggressive[8] than he had intended[9].

"Yes, yes. We thought that you might like a hint[10] of the atmosphere of the time when those volcanos formed."

"I like it," said the backer, enthusiastically. "I think we should keep it!"

The backer had made his money in Theme Parks throughout the civilized world.

"Good," said the Mayor, looking at Carter and licking his lips, "Shall we move on? I think lunch is ready."

7. **murmured:** /ˈmɜːməd/ spoke softly and indistinctly.
8. **aggressive:** with violence.
9. **intended:** meant.
10. **hint:** suggestion.

Elsewhere

The carcass was barely cold. The first great delicacies were cut from it with short knives of volcanic glass. Pieces were set to cook over the low fire. The rich aroma filled the small bowl of rock in which the people sat. A lone sheep looked down into the depression, called out nervously, and then turned quickly and instinctively[1] away from the frightening smell of fire and cooking meat.

XIX • The Mystery

Carter and the Mayor were sitting in Carter's office. "Tell me something, Mayor." Carter looked at his drink of Pisco Sour, for which he was developing a taste[1], under the Mayor's guidance, "Do you think there is a deep mystery about this island? I've been wandering around in my spare time looking at this little place of yours. There are hundreds of statues. There are those stone 'burial platforms' – you're right, they are beautifully made. All this labour, all this effort – where did it come from? Who did it?"

Mayor Pro Tem sat up straighter in his chair. He stroked[2] his chin with a strong finger, but said nothing.

"OK, Mayor, let me put it another way. I grew up in farming. I know just how much food you can grow in what area, on what sort of land, with what climate. I can't see it. There couldn't be enough food! Where did all these statues and the rest of it come from?"

1. **instinctively:** without thinking, automatically, intuitively.
1. **taste:** here, liking for.
2. **stroked:** rubbed gently.

XX • An Answer

"Selwyn, are you familiar with the works of Sir Arthur Conan Doyle?"

"Who?"

"You know, the man who wrote the Sherlock Holmes detective stories."

"Aw, yeah, you mean all those films – The Hound of the Baskervilles, and all that. Yeah, of course I've heard of him."

"Well," The Mayor took a sip[1] of his drink, "Sherlock Holmes, one of the greatest analytical minds of fiction, said that 'once you have eliminated the impossible, what you are left with, however improbable, must be the truth'."

"What does that mean?" demanded Carter, unwilling to think it through himself.

"Let's look at the facts. I think you are correct in your statement that the area of fertile[2] land here could not support sufficient skilled workers to produce all those fine statues and platforms – they are called 'moais' and 'ahus', by the way. Secondly, this island is so far away from even the nearest land mass, that we can rule out all but chance[3] visitors. I think that for a thousand years or so, it must have been effectively cut off from the rest of the world. It was a self-contained society.

"Shortly after we first met, Selwyn, I showed you the sort of tool used by the people who did all this work. I imagine that each statue took years to carve out of the rock, even with a sizeable work force. How

1. **sip:** very small mouthful.
2. **fertile:** here, capable of growing crops or strong plant life.
3. **chance:** here, accidental.

34

could there ever have been enough food to feed enough people for long enough to do all this work?"

"Spacemen?" said Carter, ironically.

"I think we can dismiss the idea of creatures from another planet, Selwyn. Would anyone with the technology to travel through space carve out statues with thousands of little stone picks[4]? I don't think so."

Carter smiled, pleasantly. The alcohol in his stomach gave him a pleasant, relaxed feeling.

The Mayor continued, "OK, let's follow the formula described by Holmes. Once we have eliminated the impossible – the ideas about spaceships and the 'Lost City of Atlantis'; fantastic lost technologies of levitation[5], etc., we are left with the improbable."

"And what is that, Mayor Pro Tem?" laughed Carter. Carter thought to himself that he really should consider getting this Pisco spirit made in bulk[6] and exported.

XXI • The Improbable

"That, my friend, the inhabitants did this work. They did it over the long centuries. They could not grow enough of their sweet potatoes, fish enough food from the sea, or keep enough live-stock to feed the food-producers and the large force of stone-workers, but that they did eat – they did have enough food."

4. **picks:** a tool with a cutting or splitting edge on a length of wood.
5. **levitation:** lifting by cancelling the effect of gravity.
6. **made in bulk:** mass produced.

Carter looked thoroughly confused[1]. "OK, I hear what you say, Mayor. I agree with your reasoning: they couldn't produce enough food, but they did the work anyway. So, where does this leave us? It's a mystery. That's what I said in the first place, remember. That is the mystery of Easter Island. Admit it. It's all impossible, eh?"

"You don't have to walk far out of that door, Mr Carter, to come upon solid proof[2] that it was possible."

"So, what's your solution[3] to the mystery that has puzzled some of the best brains this century? Tell me, if you're so clever."

"Certainly I will tell you. And I'm sure you'll find my 'solution' is as obvious as Holme's friend, Dr Watson, found the great detective's solutions – once they had been pointed out[4] to him."

"Go on then."

"The stone-workers fed on themselves!"

XXII • A Horrible Idea

There was silence in the room. A pot of coffee sang quietly to itself on the stove. The wind blew, unhindered[1], across the wide spaces of the great sea. A loose board rattled somewhere. Carter had a

---

1. **confused:** not able to think clearly about something.
2. **proof:** a convincing piece of evidence.
3. **solution:** here, answer.
4. **pointed out:** indicated.

1. **unhindered:** with no obstruction.

growing feeling of a deep upset in the base[2] of his stomach, as the meaning of the words spoken by the island's Mayor penetrated into some forbidden part of his wholesome, practical, God-fearing mind.

"You mean – you don't mean – you mean…"

"Yes. The people who worked in the quarries and along the roads of this island – these people – they ate their own dead!"

"But, but…"

"It makes sense, Selwyn. The people who made all this were driven[3] at the deepest level, by faith[4], by ambition[5], by fear – whatever.

"They ate humans! They were cannibals!" The American's revulsion[6] at the thought of consuming the dead bodies of one's fellow man sickened him.

Mayor Pro Tem watched Carter. It would never occur to[7] Carter that the businessman fed everyday on the bodies of the living. Where did he think the profits came from?

"However, Carter, I suspect[8] that they rarely had to resort to[9] 'killing for the pot'. We both know just how dangerous the 'construction industry' is, don't we? And you've seen how fast we islanders distribute any extra food!"

A sudden, terrible thought half formed in Carter's numbed[10] brain.

2. **base:** here, the bottom.
3. **driven:** here, motivated.
4. **faith:** belief.
5. **ambition:** a strong desire to achieve something.
6. **revulsion:** very strong dislike.
7. **occur to:** /əˈkɜː/ here, come into the mind of.
8. **suspect:** here, think it is probably true.
9. **resort to:** do something undesirable because of necessity.
10. **numbed:** deadened of all feeling.

"Where the hell are those two bodies, damn you?" he shouted, wild eyed.

The Mayor laughed.

"Relax, Selwyn, what can you be thinking? That we've eaten them? Relax. In that great phrase, used by the American Mafia to describe the fate of their enemies, 'they sleep with the fishes'."

To the American, the idea that the Mayor had arranged[11] for the bodies of the two dead environmentalists to be stolen and thrown into the sea, to be swept[12] away on some great ocean current[13], seemed immensely preferable to what had flown into his head moments before. Ruthlessness[14] Carter could understand. The world steadied around him.

"Yes, Selwyn I thought we might ask the relatives to give permission[15] for them to be buried here in the land they died to help protect. If they do, we'll bury a couple of boxes of stones in the churchyard, and erect[16] fine memorials to them!"

"Sometimes, Mayor Pro Tem, I worry about you," said Carter, and took a long drink.

11. **arranged**: organised.
12. **swept**: carried away by a strong force.
13. **current**: a moving stream of water in a larger body of water.
14. **Ruthlessness**: /ˈruːθləsnəs/ tendency to act without moral considerations.
15. **permission**: a statement that something is allowable.
16. **erect**: put up, construct.

XXIII • New York

The grey light shone dimly through the office windows on Central Avenue in Manhattan. Through the glass wall of the manager's office, a dozen people could be seen working at computer keyboards. The distant clicking of the keys made a nervous background to the confused noise of conversations on the banks of telephones.

Walgrave, the head of the promotion[1] department for the new tourist attraction of Easter Island, sat back and stared at the row of glossy advertising posters hanging in chromium frames on the wall. To be honest, it was a thoroughly[2] boring advertising campaign[3]. Walgrave was much more at home selling 'sex' – beautiful women, youth, the images of luxury and happiness. Even the name, Easter Island, was a handicap[4]. The team had worked long and hard to educate the potential customers not to associate[5] the island with the Christian festival of 'Easter'. That was the last thing they needed: people thinking that the venue was some kind of religious pilgrimage!

Subtly[6], almost subliminally[7], they had introduced hints[8] and suggestions that there might be forms of sexual delight available on the island that were not to

---

1. **promotion:** here, concerned with creating a public appetite for.
2. **thoroughly:** completely.
3. **campaign:** /kæm'peɪn/ a set of activities to achieve one aim.
4. **handicap:** something making an activity more difficult.
5. **associate:** here, link.
6. **Subtly:** /'sʌtəlɪ/ not obviously.
7. **subliminally:** in an unseen or un-noticeable way.
8. **hints:** small indications.

be found anywhere else in the world. Any half-decent advertising executive would recognise the techniques of association and juxtaposition that had been used, but Joe and Jolene Public, the great potential market of wealthy, middle class, middle aged Americans, would feel only a slight stirring in their loins[9] – if they were still capable of such a thing – or at least a stirring of memory. It helped enormously that the hundreds of stone statues on the island were rather phallic in nature. That was a big bonus[10].

XXIV • Cheap Advertising

It had been Carter's idea. The construction costs on the island were so high, since the island was in the middle of nowhere, that the advertising and promotion budget was very tight. Carter's idea was to assemble such an interesting combination of 'Celebrities' as part of the first batch of visitors, that they would generate their own publicity.

These Celebrities would have to be paid, of course. They knew precisely why they were being invited, and would charge[1] enormous sums for their services. But, once they had been hired, it would be a simple matter to leak[2] the news of the visit to a carefully selected part of the potential market. These would come running to the door, willing to pay the high prices for

9. **stirring in their loins**: sensation of sexual excitement.
10. **bonus**: something extra.

1. **charge**: to ask as the price for something.
2. **leak**: allow to escape - here, deliberately.

this particular 'holiday of a lifetime' in the company of the rich and famous. The saving on television, magazine and billboard advertising was huge.

Walgrave didn't know why, but the saving of large amounts of money was seriously erotic. The office intercom buzzed only twice before it was answered.

"Nicky, come into my office for a moment, will you."

Nicky was young and very ambitious. He understood precisely what was required[3] as he loosened his tie. Walgrave, in her mid forties, was still an attractive woman, and power is always an aphrodisiac.

XXV • Celebrities

"We've got Stallone. We've got Kidman. We've got Whitney Houston. We've got the Cardinal of New York, and the head Rabbi. We've got the future President of the United States. We've got 'black'. We've got 'white'. What we need now is brains!"

Walgrave held the phone away from her ear as she finished speaking. She wetted the tip of her little finger with her tongue, and dabbed[1] up the last grains of white powder from the surface of her pocket mirror. She absent-mindedly rubbed her finger across her pink and healthy gums, feeling the perfect teeth, smooth and polished, below. She put the phone to her ear again.

"Carter, can you hear me?"

"Of course I can hear you! This line's so clear I could be sitting in your lap[2]!"

---

3. **required:** needed and demanded.
1. **dabbed:** touched lightly in order to pick up.
2. **lap:** the top, upper legs when someone is sitting.

"Dream on, Carter. Well, we need the 'high priest' of brains. Any ideas?"

"My best idea so far is that guy in the English University, the one that's the greatest scientific mind of his generation – Stephen Hawkins – you know, the one in the wheelchair."

"No one likes a cripple[3], Carter."

"Hang on. I'll put you on to one of the islanders. He'll sort you someone out[4]."

"Wait! I don't want to talk to some Easter Island 'hick'!"

"Miss Walgrave? Mayor Pro Tem, Easter Island 'hick', at your service."

"I'm sorry, Mr... Mayor? Do you have a Mayor?"

"I understand that you want to include someone in the promotional visit who embodies[5] the intellect – 'brains'..."

"Yes. Some symbol of academic achievement..."

"Well, Miss Walgrave, that's easy. All you have to do is make it clear, publicly and aggressively, that NO person of high academic achievement will be allowed in the first party of visitors."

"None!"

"None."

The line went quiet for a whole ten seconds.

"Mr Mayor Tempo, that's brilliant. That will cause the biggest shit-storm on the university campuses of the world since... since... well, I don't know. Tempo, you're a natural!"

"Mayor-Pro-Tem, Miss Walgrave – and you flatter[6] me."

---

3. **cripple**: a permanently physically disabled person.
4. **sort out**: here, select from a range of possibilities.
5. **embodies**: an idea or quality made physical.
6. **flatter**: give undeserved praise.

XXVI • Pro Tem

"Pro Tem?"

"Yes."

"How are your plans[1] going?"

"My plans… my plans…"

The Mayor leaned his back against the rock, and breathed a long sigh. The sun was setting in red and gold glory. The first stars were beginning to show, before the Mayor felt able to answer the question.

"Ricardo, I am worried. We have known each other since we were children. I have lived my double life as one of the islanders, on one side, and part of our family, on the other. Never before have I felt so troubled. Here we have an opportunity to provide for a safe and secure future once and for all time. Now I begin to feel that the sacrifice[2] is too great. How can it be right to destroy[3] so many lives, just to keep ourselves safe?"

Ricardo was the same age as Pro Tem. When they were children, they learned that their family was not the same as the other families on the island. They did not understand the difference, but, slowly, the difference seeped[4] into their bones, into the way that they looked at the world. In some way, they did not enjoy the innocence of the other islanders. They had a stronger sense of their family group; of the need to look after themselves; of the need to meet the foreigners head on.

No one knew quite why Pro Tem was chosen to represent the family. Perhaps he was brighter, quicker. Perhaps he

---

1. **plans:** formal intentions of how things may be done.
2. **sacrifice:** that which is given up to get something else.
3. **destroy:** wreck, or completely break.
4. **seeped:** /siːpt/ moved very gradually, like a liquid.

was just a better actor. As a child, he would imitate[5] the priest, and other leaders of the island community.

Everyone laughed at his impersonations – even the victims. Was it because he learned and remembered the mannerisms of the influential people on the island, and when they grew old, the boy preserved the memory of their vigour[6] and prime? As a young man, he stepped naturally into the shoes of the old Mayor, a man he knew so well. It was almost as if the previous Mayor was re-incarnated.

A shooting star flew, green and low, across the island sky. High up, from the corner of their eyes, the two men could see the silver dot of a satellite as it slowly crossed the heavens.

Mayor Pro Tem sighed.

"My plans are going well."

XXVII • Star

"Mr DiVinci is unable to talk to you. I'm sorry." "Mr DiVinci is standing right behind you," said Walgrave, acidly.

The public relations man just smiled slightly, and continued doing his job, protecting the 'Star'.

Walgrave turned on her heel, beckoned Nicky to follow her, and walked directly out of the room.

"She seems angry," said DiVinci.

"Two million dollars!" said the P.R. man,

5. imitate: copy.
6. vigour: /'vɪgə/ youthful strength.

44

sarcastically[1], "What does she think we are? Beggars[2]? I asked for five."

Outside in the street, Nicky opened the passenger door of the large, open topped BMW.

"Are you angry, Angela?"

"If you want to last in this business, young man," said Walgrave as she got in, "you'll have to learn that you win some, you lose some. DiVinci's only as good as his next film. They come and go, these beautiful young men."

Nicky felt suddenly insecure and uncomfortable. He opened the driver's door, climbed in, and patted[3] the woman's knee. She did not protest[4]. "Was that a good or a bad sign," thought Nicky as he drove the car out into the Hollywood traffic.

XXVIII • In a Television Studio – Washington, USA

"Ladies and gentlemen, welcome to another edition[1] of 'For and Against', the discussion programme on 'Hot Issues[2]' affecting the people of America. With us tonight, we have Miss Angela Walgrave, from the 'Easter Island Company' – welcome, Angela – and we have Professor Phillip Estein, of the 'International Environmental Agency', based here in Washington."

1. **sarcastically:** mockingly.
2. **Beggars:** people who live by asking for things for free.
3. **patted:** gently tapped with the open palm.
4. **protest:** object.

1. **edition:** here, separate episode of a series of programmes.
2. **'Hot Issues':** slang for important and popular topics for discussion.

Angela could not help staring at the little, curly[3] wire going from the host's shirt collar to a tiny, transparent earpiece. She had to admire this singular skill of television presenters, which enabled them to present the show while receiving a string of instructions from the control room.

"The subject for tonight's debate[4] is: Easter Island – tourist heaven, or tourist victim? Angela, would you care to start?"

Angela took a deep breath, smiled confidently, and launched[5] into her prepared speech. It was a masterpiece of promotional information and environmental sensitivity.

Professor Estein sat back in his chair with unaccustomed restraint[6].

He loved the cut and thrust of debate. He knew that his problem tonight was to avoid looking too passive. The programme researchers had foolishly not asked him the most important questions.

If they had, he would have admitted[7], reluctantly, that the Easter Island Company had paid him a substantial sum of money to act as a consultant on all matters 'environmental'.

Technically, he and Angela were on the same side – the side of the great, green-backed American dollar. He and Angela, wisely[8], had prepared enough harmless fireworks for the discussion to give the

3. **curly:** coiled, or in a spiral.
4. **debate:** formal discussion.
5. **launched:** /lɔːntʃt/ set out on something in the manner of a boat or rocket.
6. **restraint:** holding of oneself back, forcibly controlling.
7. **admitted:** confirmed to be true.
8. **wisely:** very sensibly or astutely.

impression[9] that they were on opposite sides of the fence.

The Professor would come out with his public integrity[10] intact, and the Easter Island company would enjoy nineteen minutes of free, prime-time TV advertising. Everyone was happy.

"Your Company is a disgrace[11], Miss Walgrave! The influx of tourists to Rapa Nui will devastate[12] the island! What have you to say to that?"

Professor Estein knew that the statement was more or less true. The tourists would destroy the island's peace, tranquillity[13], flora and fauna, and corrupt[14] the local populace.

However, he had coached[15] Angela carefully. She would skilfully undermine his arguments and statistics.

"My dear Phillip, we have set aside up to fifteen per cent of the profits from this adventure of a lifetime to specifically care for the island. That it one thousand per cent more than you were able to secure for the poor, untouched islands that Leonardo DiVinci advertised so widely in his film, 'The Beach'. Furthermore…"

The debate followed its carefully plotted[16] course.

---

9. **give the impression:** to behave in such a way as to make the observer think something.
10. **integrity:** here, reputation for honesty.
11. **disgrace:** dishonourable and out of favour.
12. **devastate:** wreck or cause substantial damage to.
13. **tranquillity:** peacefulness and calm.
14. **corrupt:** destroy the innocence of.
15. **coached:** personally trained.
16. **plotted:** here, mapped and predicted.

Walgrave wondered if her revenge[17] on that pretty boy, Leonardo, had been a bit excessive, but she soon dismissed her discomfort with a liberal[18] dusting of white powder as soon as she was alone.

XXIX • The Cave

*T*he burning torches[1] *lit the cave walls nearby, but the light failed to reach into the darkness beyond. The walls were of volcanic glass. The cave must have been left by a great volume of compressed gas held within a body of super-heated molten rock.*

The torchlight flickered over strange markings on the rock faces. Weird composites[2] of human and bird shapes crawled[3] over the shiny surfaces. The floor was of granular white dust.

The strangest thing was the sound. The echoes of the slightest noise reverberated[4] in the huge unseen space within the cavern. One of the torches moved.

It became clear that what had appeared to be the floor of the cave, was in fact a broad ledge[5] high up above a sickening drop. Far down in the blackness, there was the faintest sound of a heavy body of thick water, moving in

17. **revenge:** paying back for some injury.
18. **liberal:** here, generous.
1. **torches:** hand-held source of light.
2. **composites:** things made by combining bits of other things.
3. **crawled:** /krɔːld/ moved with the body near the ground.
4. **reverberated:** echoed.
5. **ledge:** horizontal surface with a drop at the edge.

a slow, even rhythm. It was as if the cavern itself was breathing like a massive, volcanic lung.

The men stood in the space, soaking the whole of history in through their scarred skin. The shadows were an absolute black. The still figures of 'birdmen' carved onto the rock, appeared to whirl and soar[6] about them, as if kept up by the steady breath from the deep pit[7]. The words that the men spoke among themselves were less acts of communication, than the stretching of long unused muscles. The words carried and found themselves at home, perfectly matched to this hidden place of natural calm[8]; eternal darkness.

A strong hand sent a torch out over the pit. It roared as it fell downwards, light glittering back from the walls. After a handful of heartbeats, the flaming wood hit the surface. The noise of the hard torch striking a firm, sticky layer, echoed and grew up into a great bellow[9] of sound. It faded into a long murmur[10]. There was a hiss. The light from below failed and died. The last thing was the bubble of heavy liquid covering and consuming. Then, nothing but the cavern's own breath.

6. **whirl and soar:** /wɜːl / /sɔː/ spin and glide.
7. **pit:** a deep, enclosed space.
8. **calm:** not agitated or excited.
9. **bellow:** /'beləʊ/ loud noise like angry cattle.
10. **murmur:** soft, indistinct noise.

xxx • Take-off

The day had finally come. After months of building, after weeks of careful promotion and preparation, everything was ready. A fleet of planes, hired especially for this day, taxied into position for take-off. From the great land mass of North America, from the busy Los Angeles airport, the aircraft were aimed[1] for a tiny spot in the Pacific Ocean.

Not wishing to 'put all their eggs in one basket', the insurance company had insisted that the 'Celebrities' should be divided up among the planes. This pleased the other passengers, who realised that, behind the curtained-off section at the front of First-Class, was their share of the 'great and the good'.

The first plane stood at the end of the runway, waiting for permission to take off. The powerful engines whined[2] at half throttle. The machine pulled against the braked wheels. The engine noise increased to a roar[3]. The brakes were released. The runway lights started to move past the windows. The passengers felt themselves pushed back into their seats. The nose lifted off the ground. Suddenly, the thrash and bump of the tyres on the concrete runway ceased. They were airborne. The plane flew out over the sea, climbing higher and higher. The pilot's intercom crackled on, telling the passengers nothing they did not already know. A team of hostesses, painted and efficient, moved among the wealthy passengers.

Everything, in appearance, was free.

1. **aimed:** pointed at or directed at.
2. **whined:** /waɪnd/ a high, annoying noise, lower than a scream.
3. **roar:** loud, hard, broad sound.

Everything, in fact, was very expensive.

The plane, with its precious cargo[4], flew south and to the west.

A nervous traveller counted her beads, lips moving with the silent prayers.

The plane ferried the American Dream, an ageing apartheid of privilege and success.

XXXI • Father

"Father... help me." There was no reply. The church was empty. The priest knelt at the rail[1] before the altar[2] and tried to pray.

"Father... help me."

The priest felt helpless. He felt useless. He thought of the ancient warrior priests of the early Christian Church, taking up their weapons to fight the battles of the One True God – or, should it be: their One True God?

For years, conscientious[3], patient, strong and generous, he had given the best spiritual guidance he could find in the scriptures[4] and in the examination of his own heart. He had given it day and night to the people on this island he loved. Now, he was adrift in an empty sea. He prayed for guidance.

What did he fear?

He was not a man of worldly politics. He thought

4. **cargo:** goods carried in a ship or plane.

1. **rail:** horizontal bar dividing areas.

2. **altar:** sacred table in church.

3. **conscientious:** /kɒnʃɪˈenʃəs/ self regulated to high, personal standards.

4. **scriptures:** holy writings.

his job was to guide people to live righteous lives, no matter what their external circumstances were. The circumstances in which his parishioners[5] lived, changed with time. The injustices of mankind shifted[6], began and ended.

No, this was different. He was old. He was tired. The new priests learned to be guides to God. When the Father had trained to be a priest, the teaching was different. He learned about the Devil. He learned about the old gods of the earth, the air, the sea, and the blackness that could invade[7] the human heart.

"Lord, something is rising. I feel it."

"This island, Rapa Nui, has been occupied by the human race since the time of Christ, but Christ's message[8] has only been here for five or ten generations[9]. The Old Forces are deep in the rocks here. I even fear that some of the islanders have more faith in the old gods, than in the One True God."

The priest sank back on his heels. His arms fell loose in his lap.

"Something is rising, Lord. Something is stirring in the depths. I feel the breath of darkness in the family of Pro Tem. I fear for their souls[10]."

5. **parishioners:** /pæˈrɪʃənəz/ people belonging to an individual church.
6. **shifted:** moved.
7. **invade:** occupy and take over.
8. **message:** here, teaching.
9. **generations:** about twenty five years - the time from birth to reproduction.
10. **souls:** immortal part of a person.

XXXII • Landing

The pilots of the planes entered into the spirit of the occasion, and treated their passengers to a view of their destination from the air. They circled slowly over the little island in the great expanse[1] of ocean. The sun shone. The fine-weather clouds threw their shadows on the surface of the sea. All that could be seen of the island was yellow grassland and small volcanos. And, in the distance, the extended runway where they would land.

"Are we all going to fit down there?" joked one stout[2] man in a stetson[3] and pearl-buttoned cowboy shirt, "It doesn't look any bigger than one of my farms!"

Yes, Easter Island looked small. They had all travelled a quarter of the way round the world to arrive at this spot in the ocean.

The plane bucked[4] suddenly.

"Sorry, ladies and gentlemen, we are experiencing a small amount of turbulence. Please return to your seats, fasten your safety belts, and prepare for landing."

The touch-down was perfect. As soon as the wheels hit the runway, the Captain reversed the thrust[5] on the engines and the plane slowed quickly.

Five minutes later, the passengers were comfortably sipping drinks in the reception lounge. The Government of Chile had waived[6] its rights to

1. **expanse:** wide area.
2. **stout:** fat or thick bodied.
3. **stetson:** cowboy hat.
4. **bucked:** moved suddenly up.
5. **thrust:** hard push.
6. **waived:** did not claim the right to do something.

inspect passports and luggage. Everything was as smooth as could be.

Walgrave, Carter and the rest, moved through the assembly, shaking hands, slapping backs, and generally smiling and joking with the first customers of this giant new enterprise[7]. Already the eyes of many of the men were gazing around to see if they could see the selection of beautiful, 'single' women, available by the night. The Easter Island Company intended to satisfy all the usual appetites of the visitors.

Mayor Pro Tem was nowhere to be seen. Carter noticed his absence. He had become accustomed[8] to the company of the big man, the friend to all, the surprisingly skilled[9] solver of a host[10] of problems. Carter felt a little exposed. Still, everyone needs to spend some time with their family. Perhaps the Mayor was just being discreet[11] and considerate. Carter could still remember the unfavourable impression Mayor Pro Tem had made on him when they first met. Good man!

XXXIII • The Great Day

Carter was a natural performer. He was as happy as a man who had lost a dollar and found a gold credit card with the PIN number written on the back. The crowd of visitors responded to him warmly.

7. **enterprise:** commercial operation.
8. **accustomed:** used to.
9. **skilled:** able and experienced.
10. **host:** here, a large number.
11. **discreet:** sensitive to other people's feelings.

He made little jokes about the already well publicised habits[1] of the film stars and celebrities who stood smiling near the front of the small stage[2].

He introduced the island. Quite a lot of it could be seen from where they stood, in a natural amphitheatre on the lower slope of Rapa Nui, near the hotel village where they were staying.

He pointed out a group of safari-suited[3] men and women who were the 'expert guides' ready to answer any query about the island. They would not, of course, be able to supply the answer to the 'Secret of Easter Island' – and, if any one of them tried, the visitors should inform Carter himself as soon as possible, so that the fraud[4] could be caught and roasted for the evening meal!

"He's good," said Walgrave to her new companion, "I have to say, he's very good."

"Ladies and gentlemen," Carter lifted his arms to make sure he had every-one's attention. "This is an important announcement."

The crowd quietened. Even the people who had been examining their favourite celebrities, or desperately trying to work out who they all were, ceased their constant staring, and merely glanced, now and then. The man on the stage continued.

"You all know, I am sure, that this trip is not entirely without risk[5]. You brave people would not be here if it was, I think. You would be out sunning yourself on

1. **habits:** repeated behaviour.
2. **stage:** a raised platform for communicating with a crowd.
3. **safari-suited:** dressed in jacket and trousers first designed for use when hunting in hot countries.
4. **fraud:** here, a person trying to deceive.
5. **risk:** danger.

the beaches of Monaco, and wondering where to go for your food poisoning[6] that night! No... no... There are risks here. You all, I hope, have taken out sufficient insurance against any accident.

"You will notice, ladies and gentlemen, that the guides are passing among you and handing out small devices to clip onto your belt or shirt. Each one of these devices has a large button in the centre. When this button is pressed, like this – can you see? – you will be in direct contact with a large group of very friendly operators, day and night, who will help you with any problem – any problem at all – from taps left running in your bathrooms, to the need for an immediate application of a stronger sun tan cream.

"In addition, each transmitter is automatically tracked[7] by our central computer, to ensure that no-one is lost or abandoned[8]. I must ask some of you more vigorous gentlemen at the back to leave them in your rooms when you go out on your 'night adventures' – to save embarrassment to our more sensitive operators."

The crowd laughed.

XXXIV • The Announcement

A large man edged his way through the smiling crowd. His face was a picture of friendliness and calm.

Carter saw the Mayor coming.

"Ah, good people, we have a visit from the Mayor

6. **poisoning:** illness due to unclean or unhealthy food.
7. **tracked:** followed or traced.
8. **abandoned:** deserted, or left alone and without help.

of Easter Island, Mayor Pro Tem. Perhaps he will be good enough to step up here and say a few words before we all start our tours. He is a wonderful man, but I would not advise you to accept, as I did, one of his Pisco Sour drinks. They are rather habit forming! Mayor Pro Tem... please..."

The man in the cowboy shirt and hat turned to his wife, and said,

"Did I hear right, Winnie, 'piss-go-sour? That doesn't sound too good!'"

"It's probably Spanish for something or other, dear. The locals here speak Spanish. I met some of them early this morning in the little village down the hill. They're polite; polite and friendly."

The Mayor, by this time, had climbed onto the stage, shaken Carter by the hand, and moved in front of the microphone. His voice, through the public address system, boomed across the open ground.

"Hello, visitors. Welcome to Rapa Nui. We have waited, I must admit, rather nervously, for your arrival. Happily, everything is ready for you. You probably know quite a lot about our island already, from the booklets and promotional videos you have seen."

The Mayor paused, and reached into his pocket. He looked down at a small object in his hand. He took a breath, and went on,

"I hear that everything in America is very big and grand. It would be difficult to impress you with the size of the monuments here. There are many statues and platforms, but it is difficult for the visitor to understand what they represent.

"I have a suggestion. I think we can trust you to leave the island as you find it. I have in my hand a small stone. There are thousands of stones like this about the island, especially near the quarry where the statues were carved. When you are at the quarry, find one of these stones. Pick it up for a while, go to the rock face in the quarry, and strike your stone against the rock. Look carefully at the mark you have made. That mark will be there for ever. Leave the stone on Easter Island, with your own mark on the rock face."

There was a puzzled silence throughout the many hundreds of American tourists.

"Visitors, the people who made everything on this island knew nothing about any metals. They were 'stone-age' people. They tied this stone – yes, this very stone – to a short piece of wood, and used this small pick to fashion the statues.

"Think about this. You will start to get a feel[1] for the island."

XXXV • The Offer

Mayor Pro Tem stood looking out over his audience. He bit his lip. It was now or never.

"My family and I – one of the oldest on the island of Rapa Nui – wish to make you all an offer[1]…"

Carter looked across at the Mayor. What was this? What offer could the Mayor possibly make? Two thousand Pisco Sours!

"I cannot tell you the secret of Easter Island. I do not know it. Perhaps no one ever will. The writings

1. **get a feel:** here, become sensitive to the qualities of.
1. **offer:** hold up something for acceptance.

left by the earlier inhabitants have defied[2] all attempts to decipher them. What I can do, is offer to show you a secret and wonderful place on the island, which is known only to the elders of my extended family. No outsider has ever seen this place. As a memorial to the great changes faced by this island, I offer to make you a part of the great memorial – to show you something that no-one from outside this island has ever seen. In a way, you will become part of the island."

A great cheer went up from the listeners. Carter could only smile and look on.

The Mayor of Rapa Nui gently lifted his hands.

"I fear that it will be too difficult for anyone who is not reasonably fit to enter this place. Also, we ask that no cameras or video equipment be taken along. It is for your eyes alone."

XXXVI • The Secret Place

In the end, nearly eight hundred people considered themselves to be strong enough to take up the offer. The event was to occur the next evening. Mayor Pro Tem would say nothing about the location[1]. He had told the people he would guide them. That is what he would do.

Throughout the day, the visitors sampled[2] all that the Easter Island Company could offer. They were

2. **defied:** /dɪˈfaɪd/ here, resisted.
1. **location:** place.
2. **sampled:** tried.

ferried around the island, examining the statues and platforms, and the strange carvings on rock faces. It seemed that Mayor Pro Tem's offer of a special 'wonder' on the following day freed everyone from the obligation[3] to be completely impressed by what they saw on this day. In a way, everything became more enjoyable, more impressive. Somehow, the tourists had been slowed down from their usual speed, and were now more in harmony with the pace[4] of life on the island.

With a stone pick-head in their hands, they sensed the intensity and duration of the work that had been carried out on the island. They looked more closely at the finish on the surfaces of the statues and platforms. They started to wonder at all that had been achieved[5] with so little. The sense of aloneness in the great ocean made itself felt. They were quieter and more thoughtful. Even the flirtations[6] between the holiday-makers became calmer.

XXXVII • The Day

The day dawned. The sun climbed steadily across the sky. Soon, it was evening.

There was a buzz of anticipation[1] from the waiting crowd. Several of the celebrities were asleep in their

3. **obligation:** compulsion.
4. **pace:** speed.
5. **achieved:** /ə'tʃiːvd/ managed or done, completed.
6. **flirtations:** playing at love.
1. **anticipation:** expectation.

beds. Their absence was not noticed. They would miss the trip.

Carter was ecstatic. This was an unexpected boost to the visitors' enjoyment of the island. He realised that it was a 'one off'. This experience would never be repeated.

The light was fading. Fifteen men appeared, walking through the trees. As they came nearer, it was clear that they were all completely naked.

A subdued[2] gasp went up from the waiting Americans. Each of the fifteen naked men carried an unlit torch – a bundle of twigs, soaked in oil and tied to a length of heavy wood.

Carter stood, mouth open, staring.

The men walked among the gathered tourists. Their bodies were covered in a tracery[3] of pale, long-healed scars. Some of the men had deep grooves[4] of old injuries about their bodies. At their head was Pro Tem.

Carter spluttered to life, "Mayor! Those marks! You're all covered with scars. What in God's name has happened to you all?"

Pro Tem looked into Carter's eyes.

"I fear that if you swim in the sea off this coast, the water you swim in will always be red."

"What?… Oh!"

Pro Tem stood there in front of Carter. Carter experienced a strange sensation of shifting images. Months ago, he thought the Mayor looked like Harvey Keitel, the American actor. Now, he realised

2. **subdued:** quiet and held back.
3. **tracery:** fine network.
4. **grooves:** narrow, long depressions.

that Mayor Pro Tem looked nothing less that the physical incarnation[5] of the statues that stood in their hundreds, watching the island.

Carter had a sense of vertigo[6] at the thought that Easter Island might contain a living, thriving link with the lost past.

"Come, American, we are going to the crater of Rana Koi."

Pro Tem smiled a sad smile, and turned away, followed closely by his people.

The islanders started off up the slope. Eight hundred people, visiting this world of volcanos, statues and lost history, followed in their footsteps.

Half way up to the rim of the volcano, near an outcrop[7] of rock, Mayor Pro Tem disappeared into the steeply sloping ground.

"Jesus!" swore Carter, "It's like the 'Pied Piper of Hamelyn' taking the children into the mountain!"

XXXVIII • The Entrance

The entrance to the tunnel was hidden by a bush. Once you knew it was there, it was an easy matter to step round the bush and duck[1] into the low entrance of the straight, smooth-walled tunnel.

For a hundred metres or more, the islanders and the visitors felt their way forward along the dark tunnel.

5. **incarnation:** made human.
6. **vertigo:** feeling of falling.
7. **outcrop:** a piece sticking out.
1. **duck:** here, to lower the head suddenly.

When they stepped out into the evening twilight near the floor of the crater, it seemed like the brightest day.

The small areas of clear water among the thick growth of reeds on the crater floor, shone brightly as they reflected the deep ultramarine of the sky.

Pro Tem set out around the edge of the crater's marshy[2] floor. The crowd followed in his footsteps. No one spoke.

Pro Tem's companions held back, following a little way behind the Americans.

When he was below the part of the volcano rim which faced the ocean, Pro Tem stopped and turned, waiting. The large group collected itself in front of him.

The naked islanders each moved to a pile of firewood heaped at intervals round the space where the Americans were standing. Their torches sprang to life. When the flames touched the firewood, it caught light quickly, filling the edge of the crater with a primitive fire.

Pro Tem looked up at the sky; up at the ancient, ever-changing sky.

It was time.

2. **marshy:** of earth which is soft and full of water.

XXXIX • Into the Cavern

The way into the cavern was concealed by a huge rock. The entrance was low. One of the islanders went ahead with a torch. In its light, the walls shone, carved with the work of a hundred stone picks. Pro Tem followed. Then Carter.

Carter heard another torch flaring behind him. The light bounced drunken shadows on to the walls. American voices murmured far behind.

Suddenly, the space opened out. The walls and roof disappeared from view. The torch-light could not penetrate[1] the darkness. Every noise echoed as in a great cathedral[2]. Voices were lowered to whispers.

"Be careful, Carter," said Pro Tem, holding the American back with one hand, "One more step, and you will fall into the great pit." The Mayor waved his torch out over the edge of the ledge on which they were standing. Carter drew in his breath, sharply.

More and more Americans were reaching the edge, held back by the islanders, their torches flickering and spitting.

"What's that noise down there?" asked Carter. His voice was nervous and strained[3]. He was a man alone. The tourists accepted everything: the appearance of the islanders, and their strange journey. They accepted without question. It was all part of a bizarre[4] entertainment.

Only Carter sensed that his country-people were completely and dangerously wrong. The rules of their

1. **penetrate:** push into.
2. **cathedral:** very large and important church.
3. **strained:** under stress.
4. **bizarre:** very strange.

civilization did not reach this huge cavern below the dead volcano.

"Down there?" Pro Tem seemed distant, preoccupied, "Down there is the answer to many mysteries. The sound you hear is the heavy movement of an almost solid body of water. The sea pushes into the pit through a tiny hole no bigger than a man can squeeze through. This hole is far below the surface.

"For thousands of years, the sea has flowed in and out with the beating of the waves against the cliffs. Fish are carried through the hole and into the pit. At one time they could swim out when the water retreated. But, slowly, over the centuries, the surface water in the pit evaporated. The water became saltier. Eventually, the salt was so concentrated that it started to form crystals."

Carter listened intently.

"The top layer, for twice the height of a man, is almost solid salt. The sea creatures carried into the pit, are poisoned by the salt. They can't breathe. They die, float towards the surface, and are preserved in the layer of salt."

Pro Tem laughed. The American standing beside him, flinched[5].

Pro Tem pinched Carter's arm, and said,

"You believe that my ancestors[6] ate the flesh of their own people. Now you can know the truth. Here, below your feet, is the food that God – or our god – provided[7] so that our people could concentrate on the stone carving. Salted fish, Carter, salted fish!"

5. **flinched:** drew back suddenly, as if about to be hit.
6. **ancestors:** /ˈænsestəz/ people from whom one is descended.
7. **provided:** given.

Pro Tem moved his strong hand to Carter's shoulder. Carter looked down at the scars on the man's arm. The Mayor followed his gaze.

"Ah, Carter, the 'Birdmen'. They did not risk[8] their lives to collect a single egg. They swam down in the beating surf, down to the hole leading to the pit. Each springtime, when the fish were swarming[9], they cleared away any debris which was blocking the hole. The Birdmen did this so that the people would not starve. My brothers here have all done the same" The man's voice dropped to a whisper, "We have survived." Carter thought of the sharp, volcanic rocks in the sea, and shivered.

A low noise started in the cave. It was some time before the American visitors realised that it was the sound of the islander's voices.

The strange, rounded words sang and played in the great space. Each islander had a different word to sing. Each word was matched[10] to the position from which it was sung. Each word resonated[11], tuned to the way its particular echoes ran back and forth. The sum of all the fragments[12] grew to become a great, roaring wall of sound. The cavern vibrated.

The walls of the cavern, which looked so solid, were, in fact, covered with a fine tracery of cracks – a tracery as fine as the scars on the bodies of the men with torches. The whole cavern was an assembly of slabs and blocks, of isolated pieces of rock, standing

8. **risk**: put in danger.
9. **swarming**: moving in large numbers.
10. **matched**: suited.
11. **resonated**: rang in tune or harmony.
12. **fragments**: small pieces from something large.

like a great 'house of cards'[13]. The noise from the throats of the islanders, amplified in the enclosed space, started to disturb the fine, ancient balance.

Here and there, a stone shook away from the roof and crashed to the floor, or hurtled[14] into the pit.

And then a huge slab fell from the wall. The impact on the floor was terrific, upsetting the deep balance of the whole cavern. The fine cracks on the walls widened, like a mirror cracking to pieces.

The danger was clear. The whole huge space was collapsing in on itself.

A scream was frozen in hundreds of throats.

XL • STOP!

"STOP!" The single voice was discordant. It seemed to break the spell[1]. The noise tumbled[2] and died away. The echoes rang and slowly ran away to nothing. The shifting of the cave halted. The pit breathed.

The voice that had shouted, now became a tortured[3] whisper. It was as if the island was dying with the echoes.

Pro Tem turned to his family members. "Stop, my friends. We cannot do this thing. The sacrifice is too great. It is too much!"

---

13. **'house of cards'**: a way of expressing instability, literally, a structure built of playing cards resting on each other.
14. **hurtled**: rushed or fell very quickly.
1. **spell**: here, a fixed state as if held by magic.
2. **tumbled**: fell in a rolling way.
3. **tortured**: pained.

With a sigh, Pro Tem let the torch fall from his hand. Carter jumped back in alarm[4]. His foot slipped into a crack in the white powdered floor. With a cry of fear, he lost his balance.

He tumbled into space, silent. Pro Tem grabbed[5] his torch and jumped straight down after him, bracing[6] himself for the impact on the salt-laden water, which waited in the pit.

Pro Tem fell feet first, crashing up to his shoulders in the crystal water. His torch blazed and sizzled in front of his face, blinding him to all but its hot flames. He seized it, and jammed it, base down, to stand upright in the semi-solid of salt and water.

Where was Carter? There was no sign on the watery surface to tell where the American had fallen. Pro Tem swept his hands backwards and forwards, searching for a soft area through which a body had crashed. He struggled[7] round, half blinded by the salt in his eyes. Here, here was the place. He took a breath, and dragged[8] himself below the surface, searching, in the eternal fellowship of humanity, for the man in need of his help. His hands reached out, pushing aside the salt crystals. Nothing. He forced himself deeper, like a man drowning himself in mud. Nothing.

Then he felt something. He seized it. His fingers sank into the soft, preserved flesh of a huge fish. Again, and again. Then his wrist knocked on bone. Pro Tem, his lungs screaming for air, his stomach

4. **alarm:** here, a state of fear.
5. **grabbed:** took hold of quickly and firmly.
6. **bracing:** here, holding steady or rigid in preparation.
7. **struggled:** moved with difficulty.
8. **dragged:** pulled with difficulty.

churning from the swallowed salt, dragged the American upwards towards the surface.

Carter choked[9] and spluttered into life like a new-born baby. His breath came in rasping heaves[10]. He tried to wipe away the clinging, burning salt. The torch burnt still, tipped over at a crazy angle.

High above, Walgrave stripped off her clothes and started tying them together. Other people joined in. Soon, a rope of safari suits began to descend to the pair trapped[11] in the pit. There was even a pearl-buttoned shirt in the line of clothes.

XLI • The Truth

"We haven't much time, Mayor Pro Tem." Carter looked at the other man, sunk deep in the crystalline water. He coughed, and spat.

"I want the truth. I have no right[1] to demand it — you saved my life, I am in your debt — but I want the truth. You brought us here to kill us all, didn't you? You were prepared[2] to sacrifice yourselves to destroy us. That noise you made. You were causing the whole cavern to resonate. It would have shaken itself to pieces. We would all have died, crushed by thousands of tonnes of rock, or drowned down here in this hell-hole of salt water."

9. **choked:** tried to breathe with an obstruction in the throat.
10. **rasping heaves:** scraping, violent pushes.
11. **trapped:** unable to escape or get out.

1. **right:** here, moral, implied permission to do something.
2. **prepared:** ready to do something.

Pro Tem said nothing.

"You're a heartless piece of work, Pro Tem. At least I felt guilty[3] about what happened to the bodies of those two environmentalists! You…"

"I arranged for them to be stored in our small island hospital, until they could be buried, decently[4], in the churchyard."

"You said…!"

"I know what I said."

Carter was confused. He was glad to be alive, but he could not read the face of this man bathed in the light of the torch. It was important that he did understand.

"If you had killed us all, it would be the end of the Easter Island Company. You could live in peace forever – not you, personally, of course."

There was a pause, and then both men burst out laughing. Both had been delivered from death. Both men breathed. The blood pumped[5] in their veins.

"So, my friend, Mayor Pro Tem, why didn't you do it? Tell me."

The long line of clothes had almost reached them.

"Carter, something has been troubling me for days. When the singing up there became one huge noise, for some reason, it made me think of you."

"You were about to kill me, and you were thinking of me – thanks!" exclaimed Carter, sarcastically.

"And then I realised, Carter. I realised that this tourist business was never meant to work. You never intended the business to survive. It was always just a big noise, a way of getting a huge amount of money

---

3. **guilty:** mentally responsible for some wrong action.
4. **decently:** in a good, proper way.
5. **pumped:** pushed through in a series of movements.

to go from one place to another. And you were in the middle, taking a cut of every dollar that moved. Those investors are never going to see their money again, are they?"

Carter laughed.

"You're a smart man, Mayor. I didn't realise how important to me that would be – if you weren't smart, we'd both be dead!"

The mayor smiled grimly, "You knew that the great American tourist trips to Easter Island would not last long."

"And you'd be left with a nice new hospital, and a number of useful bits and pieces. Everyone would be happy!"

Mayor Pro Tem looked like a man who, for all the right reasons, had very nearly made a disastrous mistake. When he thought of it, sweat covered his face.

"Let's go, Mayor. I'm afraid your cave is falling to bits. No more salted fish for you!"

"Right now, I'd settle for a very large Pisco Sour. After you, Carter" said Pro Tem, helping the American get a good hold on the rope of safari suits.

"Mayor, I need a holiday."

"Selwyn, have you considered Monaco?"

Remember to use your dictionary to check the definition of any words you don't know.

CHAPTERS I-X

PRE-READING QUESTIONS

1) What do you already know about Easter Island?
2) Look at the picture of the statue Moai, Ahu Vaiuri at Tahai. What do you think the statue was for?

AFTER YOU HAVE READ CHAPTERS I-X

1) Answer the questions.

a) Why does Mayor Pro Tem cultivate his image as an odious man?
b) Who is Carter?
c) What sort of person does Carter think Pro Tem is at the beginning of the story?
d) Who was the 'Bird-man'?
e) What is strange about the skin on Pro Tem's arms?
f) How were the statues made?
g) What is the second thing Pro Tem wants Carter to understand when he takes him out to see the island?
h) How do the developers want to transform Easter Island?
i) How do the local people react to the development?

2) Find the words in the box below that correspond to the following definitions. All the words come from chapters I-X.

a) speaking with very few words
b) contracted in tight wrinkles (usually the lips)
c) without humour, very seriously
d) dull, cold and comfortless
e) people who come to live in a place, not as tourists
f) live and grow successfully
g) a place where rock is dug from the ground
h) protected (from the weather)
i) an attempt to achieve something
j) confidence and faith in something

T	S	T	X	H	D	E	S	R	U	P
R	E	R	S	N	F	K	L	G	I	U
U	D	E	V	I	R	H	T	O	D	G
S	R	U	O	V	A	E	D	N	E	R
T	R	C	O	R	W	O	Y	I	R	I
S	F	U	I	T	S	L	R	U	E	M
B	E	V	H	H	A	L	R	H	T	L
L	A	C	O	N	I	C	A	L	L	Y
E	Y	P	N	E	E	Y	U	H	E	U
A	O	U	U	S	R	G	Q	I	H	O
K	P	H	B	A	G	B	J	I	S	D
N	M	S	E	T	T	L	E	R	S	F

3) **Now write your own sentence for each of the words. You may change the form or tense of the word if necessary.**

a) ....
b) ....
c) ....
d) ....

73

e) ....

f) ....

g) ....

h) ....

i) ....

j) ....

4) **'The platforms on which the statues used to stand are made of blocks of stone.' Do the statues stand on the platforms now? Did they stand on the platforms for a brief moment, or for an extended period? If you have answered correctly, you will understand that 'used to' refers to a state or activity that existed or happened in the past over a period of time, or repeatedly, and is no longer true. Transform the pairs of sentences below into one single sentence using 'used to' or 'didn't use to' as in the example.**

a) He drank whisky in the past. He doesn't drink it now.
   He used to drink a lot of whisky.

b) She didn't smoke when she was young. Now she does.
   ....

c) 'Do you do a lot of sport?' 'I did in the past. I don't now.
   ....

d) She's very thin. She wasn't very thin in the past.
   ....

e) There is a lot of traffic in the town. There wasn't in the past.
   ....

f) There aren't many trees in the town. In the past there were a lot of them.

....

g) He has changed. He wasn't so moody in the past.

....

h) She has changed. She was more cheerful when she was a girl.

....

i) They lived in the country when they were first married. Now they live in the city.

....

5) '...the platforms, the statues, everything, were made with tools identical to the one you hold in your hand.' We often use the passive in English when we don't know exactly who did something. The passive is also used if we want to focus on the person or thing that received the action: 'The statue was placed on a platform'; or if it is obvious who performs the action: 'He was arrested last night' (obviously by the police). Rewrite the sentences below in the passive. The new subject has been written in italics.

a) They destroyed *the buildings* during the invasion.
b) They stole *the painting* from the museum.
c) Someone killed *him* in a road accident.
d) They will enlarge *the small island airport*.
e) They are building *a new hospital* for the island.
f) They were repairing *the road* when I tried to drive through the city centre.
g) Someone has informed *her* of the situation.
h) Someone will take *you* to your hotel when you arrive at the airport.
i) Someone will take *you* on a guided tour of the island.

Pre-reading questions

1) At the end of the last section Carter thinks that Pro Tem is a fool. Is this true? What do you know of his character so far?
2) What sort of special holidays do you think they are planning for the rich American tourists?

After you have read Chapters XI-XX

1) Answer the questions.

a) How does Pro Tem deal with the rude Mr. Irving?
b) What is a Sau Sau?
c) How does Pro Tem deal with the Greens?
d) How is the mayor perceived as being different by the local people?
e) How are the two people killed?
f) How does Pro Tem react to the news of the accident?
g) Why is Carter so worried about the death of the two environmentalists?
h) How does Pro Tem explain the accident to the two financial backers?

2) Complete the crossword below. All the words can be found in Chapters XI-XX.

Across
a) A cushion used to absorb a blow.
b) Make calm.
c) Replace, supplant.
d) Loose, without tension.

Down

e) A sudden, violent wind.
f) Move quickly and laterally to evade someone or avoid collision.
g) Moved fast without much control.
h) The meat or muscle on a body.
i) A loud, unpleasant sound or scream.

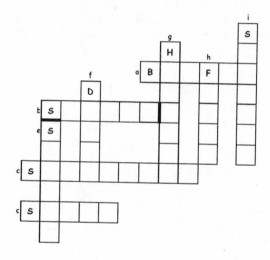

3) **Look at page 22 and read what Mayor Pro Tem says from 'Listen! Please listen....' to '... last toromiro seeds.' What tense are all the verbs? Mayor Pro Tem uses several expressions to indicate that what he says is set in the past: 'I was a boy', 'in the fifties', 'I was a young man'. The important thing is that these periods of time are <u>finished in the past</u> – Mayor Pro Tem is no longer a young man and so all the verbs must be in the past tense. Complete the sentences below by choosing the correct form of the verb.**

a) When I was young I (lived/have lived) in a small town.
b) I (lived/have lived) in this house for several years.
c) My grandfather's family (was/has been) too poor to send him to university, but, as he (was/has been) a good student, he (got/has got) a special grant and (was/has been) able to go.
d) I (studied/have studied) many languages in my life, but Russian is certainly the most difficult.
e) We (went/have been) to the Red Sea for our holiday last year, but this year we still (didn't decide/haven't decided) where to go.
f) I (read/have read) all that writer's books except for her latest novel. I (tried/have tried) to buy it yesterday, but the shop (was/has been) out of stock.

Now complete this sentence:

When the time period is not specified or not yet finished (e.g. this year) we use the _____ _____ tense, which is formed by *have/has* + the _____ _____.

4) Re-read Chapter XV, 'Death'. This chapter describes a squall, a sudden violent wind. Underline all the words and expressions which create a sense of violent, turbulent weather. What image is created at the end of this chapter? How does it make you feel?

....
....
....

5) 'There's been an accident back at the building site.' The messenger arrives with some bad news. When we give news we usually use the present perfect tense (have/has + past participle) because we are more interested in the event than in the time when it happened. Later, when we go on to give details about time and place, we usually use the past tense. For example, we could follow this sentence with 'A central lighting column fell over the building site and killed two people.' Complete the following sentences by choosing the correct form of the verb in brackets.

a) There (was/<u>has been</u>) a further increase in the price of petrol. The government (<u>announced</u>/has announced) this latest rise in a special news broadcast early this morning.

b) Some protests (already began/have already begun) at the petrol pumps. A spokesman for Smell Petroleum Company (said/has said) during a press conference, that the increases (were/have been) entirely due to government policy.

c) The world famous actress Wilma Wallace (was/has been) killed in an air crash. She (was/has been) flying one of her collection of small planes over the Rocky Mountains, when weather conditions (forced/have forced) her to make an emergency landing. The attempt (failed/has failed) and the actress (died/has died) on impact.

d) The president of the United States (announced/has announced) new measures to cut down emissions of poisonous gases in order to slow down the greenhouse effect. The announcement (was/has been) made yesterday at the world conference on the environment in Geneva.

6) 'We'll be paying cash and we'll be paying with one of the worst media fiascos ever.' The future progressive (will be ...ing) can be used to say that an action will be in progress at a particular moment in the future: 'This time tomorrow I'll be lying on the beach.' It is also used, as in the example from the book, to suggest that something in the future has already been fixed or decided, or is highly probable. Complete the sentences below and try to say in what way the future progressive is being used in each case.

a) Tomorrow is Sunday so my Grandmother .... (go) to church as usual.

b) She's a very active old lady, you can't get her to rest. She .... (take up) dance classes next.

c) It's no use phoning him now. He .... (watch) the football match.

d) At three o'clock tomorrow I .... (fly) over the Alps.

e) If you need my help, call me. I .... (work) in the next office.

f) 'Shall we invite Jane to the party?' 'Well, she's got a new baby, so she .... (probably stay) at home for New Year's Eve.'

PRE-READING QUESTIONS

a) At the end of the last section we are left with a mystery. How do *you* think the stone workers were fed?

b) Why do you think Pro Tem wants to create a feeling of mystery?

AFTER YOU HAVE READ CHAPTERS XXI-XXX

1) Answer the questions.

a) How did the stoneworkers feed themselves according to Pro Tem?

b) How does Carter react to this idea?

c) Where are the bodies of the two dead conservationists?

d) Who is Walgrave?

e) How does she try to attract American tourists to Easter Island?

f) Why are celebrities among the first batch of tourists?

g) What is Pro Tem's suggestion for the problem of finding a famous academic?

h) Why was Pro Tem chosen to represent his family?

i) Why is the TV debate 'For and Against' not a real debate?

j) Briefly describe the cave.

k) Why do the celebrities travel in several different planes?

2) Connect the words on the left with the definitions on the right. The first one has been done for you.

a) made in bulk — evidence
b) unhindered — come into the mind
c) proof — pitiless behaviour, acting without moral considerations
d) faith — lower back and sides
e) occur to — mass produced
f) numbed — with no obstacle
g) ruthlessness — belief
h) thoroughly — disabled person (unpleasant term)
i) loins — give undeserved praise
j) cripple — people who live on the streets and ask for money
k) flatter — deadened, with no feeling
l) seep — personally train
m) beggars — move on hands and knees like a baby
n) coach — shelf
o) crawl — move gradually like liquid
p) ledge — completely

Fit some of the definitions into the crossword below. Which word is spelled vertically?

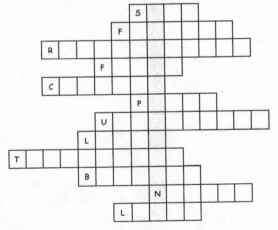

82

3) **Rhyming words. Look at the words below and choose the word from the box which rhymes with each one. Be careful. Some of the words in the box don't rhyme with anything.**

come - pig - bomb - pressed - deep - yeast - pager - tall - peg - coins - leans - health - care - towel - teeth

a) mayor ....
b) major ....
c) numb ....
d) crawl ....
e) seep ....
f) priest ....
g) beg ....
h) loins ....
i) wealth ....

4) **Say if the following statements are true or false.**

	T	F
a) Carter thinks modern business men feed on the bodies of the living.	❏	❏
b) Carter thinks that the islanders have eaten the bodies of the two conservationists.	❏	❏
c) Pro Tem has buried the bodies and put monuments over the graves.	❏	❏
d) Walgrave wants to encourage the idea of religious holidays to Easter Island.	❏	❏
e) Pro Tem thinks he is the reincarnation of the previous mayor.	❏	❏
f) Angela Walgrave and Phillip Estein know each other.	❏	❏

g) They are enemies. ❑ ❑
h) There are bird-men drawn on the walls
of the cave. ❑ ❑

5) 'The local people can't have produced enough food for themselves. They must have eaten each other.' When we make deductions about past events we use 'can't have + past participle' when talking about something impossible; 'might/ could have + past participle' when talking about a possibility; and 'must have + past participle' when talking about a certainty. Complete the following sentences with must/might/could/can't have + the past participle of a verb in the box.

> lose - drop - be - be - be - be -
> be - snow - sleep - hear

a) I can't find my ticket anywhere. I
.... it.
b) You .... when you took your handkerchief out of your pocket.
c) The streets are all white this morning. It .... during the night.
d) John is late. He .... delayed by the bad weather.
e) On the other hand he .... late. He often does.
f) That .... Mary on the phone. The call was over far too quickly and she always talks for hours.
g) You .... of the Macdonald case. It was one of the most famous murders in history.

h) Mary Macdonald married six men and killed them all for their money. She .... a very beautiful woman to convince so many men to marry her.

i) Of course you .... too young to hear about the murders, you .... more than ten at the time.

Chapters XXXI - XLI

PRE-READING QUESTIONS

a) Do you think Mayor Pro Tem is really interested in developing the island?
b) What is his real aim?

AFTER YOU HAVE READ CHAPTERS XXXI - XLI

1) Answer the questions.

a) Why does the priest feel afraid?
b) What is the first thing some of the male tourists look for on landing at Easter Island airport?
c) Why do the crowd respond warmly to Carter?
d) What small devices are handed out to all the tourists?
e) What does Pro Tem tell the visitors to do with the small stones?
f) What offer does he make them?
g) Why do the Americans gasp when they see the 15 men appear?
h) Where do they lead the tourists?
i) What did the stone workers really eat?
j) Why are the 15 men covered in scars?

k) What happens when the men start to sing?
l) Why had Pro Tem taken the tourists to the cave?
m) What did Pro Tem realise about Carter?

2) Find the words in the word box below that correspond to the following definitions.

a) A person belonging to an individual church
b) Fat or thick-bodied
c) A hard push
d) To not claim the right to do something
e) A large number
f) Prudent, cautious, unobtrusive
g) Illness due to unclean or unhealthy food
h) To try, to taste
i) To manage to do something, to attain a goal
j) Long, narrow depression
k) Soft and full of water (of earth)
l) To draw back suddenly as if to evade a blow
m) To move in large numbers like bees or ants
n) To move with difficulty, to fight

S	E	F	P	O	T	E	E	R	C	S	I	D
F	A	N	A	P	L	O	H	Q	U	A	S	P
R	E	J	R	E	V	O	O	R	G	M	F	O
T	L	W	I	S	D	R	S	O	M	P	G	I
I	G	E	S	T	O	U	T	U	A	L	B	S
E	G	S	H	R	F	E	E	R	R	E	V	O
V	U	M	I	E	M	R	A	W	S	T	W	N
I	R	J	O	S	E	V	E	I	H	C	A	I
A	T	U	N	H	U	D	B	N	Y	R	F	N
W	S	H	E	F	L	I	N	C	H	H	U	G
O	T	H	R	U	S	T	M	O	U	U	J	K

3) **Now complete the passage below using some of the words. Be careful. You may have to change the form or the tense of the words – nouns may become verbs etc.**

Detective Jones t_____ his way through the crowds that s_____ on the platform. He was a big man and a frail-looking old lady f_____ as his s_____ body pushed roughly past her. Then suddenly he saw her. She was up ahead, s_____ with a heavy suitcase and pushing her way through a h_____ of school children that had just got off the train. Detective Jones began to run. The analyses of the food s_____ taken from the woman's flat had been conclusive. Who could tell how many men she had p_____ by serving them small doses of arsenic with their evening meal. One thing was certain, if Jones managed to arrest the Fulham poisoner, it would be the greatest a_____ of his career.

4) **'In the cave, when everything is about to collapse, Pro Tem suddenly tells his family members to stop singing. They stop to listen to what he has to say.' If we look at these two sentences we see that in the first case 'stop' is followed by the 'ing' form, and in the second it is followed by the infinitive. The meaning changes. We use 'stop + ing' when we want to say that we stop an activity, or stop doing something. We use 'stop + infinitive' when we want to say that we stop one activity in order to do another. Choose the correct form of the verb in brackets in the**

sentences below. The first one has been done for you as an example.

a) I stopped (<u>working</u>/to work) as I was very tired. I stopped (having/<u>to have</u>) a coffee.

b) I usually stop (reading/to read) when my eyes get too tired.

c) I tried to do a three mile swim for charity, but I wasn't really fit enough and had to stop (swimming/to swim) after a mile and a half.

d) I was walking through the town when I saw James, so I stopped (chatting/to have a chat).

e) He stopped (reading/to read) that particular newspaper as he didn't agree with its political bias.

f) He stopped (reading/to read) the sign before he got into the lift.

g) He stopped (answering/to answer) the phone before leaving the office.

h) I wasn't getting any work done, so I had to stop (answering/to answer) the phone.

i) Stop (talking/to talk) with your mouth full.

j) Stop (making/to make) that terrible noise.

k) Stop (thinking/to think) the next time you have to make such an important decision.

5) '...he thought the Mayor looked like Harvey Keitel, the American actor.' The word 'like' often causes problems. We can say 'he likes John'; 'he looks like John'; or 'he's like John'. The first sentence suggests he and John are friends; the second that he and John are similar in appearance; and the third that they are similar in a more general way, probably for their

personalities. Complete the sentences below by choosing the correct version.

a) They are twins: they (like/look like) each other.
b) You (are just like/look just like) your father – completely unreliable!
c) I (am like/like) his brother, but I (am not like/don't like) him, even though they (are like/like) each other.
d) He (is more like/looks more like) his father because they both have black, curly hair.
e) She (is like/looks like) her sister in that they both (like/are like) sport and being out in the fresh air all the time.
f) She (isn't like/doesn't like) her brother, because he (likes/is like) reading and listening to music indoors.

6) **Re-read chapter XL from the point where Pro Tem dives into the pit to save Carter. Underline all the words and expressions which contribute to the drama of the moment.**

....
....
....

7) **Now write your own passage. Imagine you have fallen off some rocks into rough sea and are trying to get back to land. Use as many of the underlined words and expressions as possible.**

....
....
....

1) List what you think are the advantages and disadvantages of life on Rapa Nui for one of the traditional islanders:

Advantages: ....
....
....
....
....

Disadvantages: ....
....
....
....
....

2) Imagine that your job is to decide whether tourism should be expanded in Rapa Nui: write down the reasons for and against. Try to include as many positive ideas as possible.

For: ....
....
....
....
....

Against: ....
....
....
....
....

3) Imagine that Mayor Pro Tem and his family did kill the tourists and themselves. Imagine also that you are a newspaper reporter writing the story for a major newspaper in your country. Describe what happened when rescue workers arrived at the site.

....
....
....
....
....

4) What do you think personally about the tourism industry? Would you like to travel to a place like Easter Island? Do you think tourism is a threat to such places?

....
....
....
....
....

5) Think about how the story is written. How does the author try to create a sense of mystery? Did you guess what the end would be? Was the author successful in keeping it a secret? How did he achieve this?

....
....
....
....
....

6) In your opinion, what does the author think of big business people like Walgrave and Carter? Give examples from the text to support your case.

....
....
....
....
....

CONTENTS

READING WITH RICHMOND

RR	YOUNG STARTER up to 200 Headwords	STARTER 300–500 Headwords	LEVEL 1 500–600 Headwords

ADVENTURE	•Brob the Brontosaur ⓒ
	•Space Adventure ⓒ
	•Zazar ⓒ
		•Footprints in the
		  Forest ⓒ ▶
		•Holidays on Ice Ⓐ
		•Radio Boy
		•Robin Hood Ⓐ
		•Shipwrecked Sally Ⓐ ▶
		•The Pink Penguin Ⓐ
			•Adventure at
			  Piccadilly Circus Ⓐ
			•Permission to Leave

DRAMA/
STORY
	•Nessie the Monster ⓒ
	•Penelope and Tod ⓒ
	•Zazar and the
	  Seashell ⓒ
		•A Maori Story ⓒ ▶
		•Ricky Banks Music Star
		•The Channel Tunnel Ⓐ
		•The Rain Forest Ⓐ
			•Bonnie and Clyde Ⓐ
			•Escape from
			  Alcatraz Ⓐ
			•Jack's Game
			•Maria's Dilemma
			•Titanic Ⓐ

HUMOUR	•The Christmas Mouse ⓒ •Who's Coming for Tea? ⓒ •Zazar and the Fox ⓒ	•The Man from Peru	

CLASSICS		•Aladdin and other
		  stories from
		  Arabian Nights ⓒ ▶
		•The Happy Prince Ⓐ
			•A Christmas Carol Ⓐ
			•Alice in Wonderland Ⓐ
			•Puss in Boots Ⓐ

SCIENCE FICTION / FANTASY	•Merlin the Wizard ⓒ •Zazar and the Sun ⓒ	•Professor Wong & King Arthur ⓒ •Supercomputerman	•Frankenstein Ⓐ •The Vampire Ⓐ

MYSTERY/
GHOST
	•A Ghost Story ⓒ	•Dracula Ⓐ
		•Ghost Stories Ⓐ
		•The Canterville Ghost Ⓐ
			•Oscar
			•The Black Mountain
			•The Boy from
			  Yesterday
			•The Haunted
			  Castle Ⓐ

ⓒ = Colour   Ⓐ = Activity Readers   ▶ = More challenging   ⊛ = Complete and unabridged